FRANK BELLAMY'S

KING ARTHUR AND HIS KNIGHTS

THE COMPLETE ADVENTURE

TOGETHER WITH THE SWISS FAMILY ROBINSON

Edited by Steve Holland

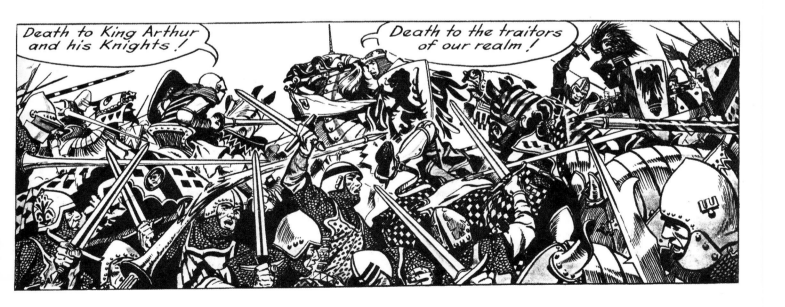

BOOK PALACE BOOKS
www.bookpalace.com

Frank Bellamy's King Arthur and his Knights: The Complete Adventure

A Book Palace Book

Published by
Book Palace Books, The Book Palace, Jubilee House
Bedwardine Road, Crystal Palace, London SE19 3AP

Tel: 020 8768 0022
email: books@bookpalace.com
web: www.bookpalace.com

Printed in China by Prolong Press Ltd

ISBN: 978-0-9551596-4-0

Copyright © The Book Palace 2008
Introduction and all artwork is © Look and Learn and is used by permission.

The Once and Future King
The Story of King Arthur

The story of King Arthur, like so many of Britain's most legendary characters, owes more to romance and poetry than historical fact. Most of us know something of the story: that Arthur pulled a sword from a stone which, according to prophecy, made him King of England; that he was taken under the wing of a wizard called Merlin; that he had a court of knights at his round table in Camelot...

But even the early legends become confused with more modern retellings. Were the legends really set in medieval England and could Arthur really have met Robin Hood? Who was the lady of the lake and did she give Arthur a sword called Excalibur or was Excalibur the sword that Arthur pulled from the stone? Did Merlin really have a wizard's duel with a witch called Madam Mim?

What we think of as 'the Arthurian legends' has changed over the years; other legends, such as that of Tristan and Iseult, have become inescapably linked with the story of Arthur and to find the historical origins of Arthur is somewhat akin to creating a statue from a block of stone and, like Michelangelo, chipping away the subsequent legends until the shape of the original figure is revealed.

The story of Arthur was first related by Geoffrey of Monmouth (c.1100-c.1155), a Welsh clergyman, who composed a history of Britain – the *Historia Regum Britanniae* (1138) – from the time of Brutus to the death of Cadwallader in the 7th century. Geoffrey himself stated that his Historia was translated (into Latin) from an ancient book written in Welsh, although his stories derive in part from the 9th century *Historia Brittonum*, itself a recension of various earlier histories which had, by Geoffrey's time, been altered and revised by other hands. Other sources were *Historia ecclesiastica gentis Anglorum* (731) by Bede and *De Excidio et Conquestu Britanniae* of Gildas the Wise, which dated from the 6th century.[1] Welsh legends and a great deal of imagination were also woven into Geoffrey's *Historia*.

From *Historia Brittonum* Geoffrey took the story of Merlin, whom he made the star of *Prophetiae Merlini*, written before 1135. Merlin was a composite figure based on Myrddin Wyllt – a 6th century Welsh bard driven mad after seeing the horrors of battle who fled to live as a wild man in a forest where he gained the powers of prophecy – and Aurelius Ambrosius – about whom the *Historia Brittonum* related the

tale of how he had been brought to the attention of the British King, Vortigern, following the collapse of a newly erected tower. Ambrosius revealed that the tower was built on an underground lake where two dragons were constantly fighting.

Geoffrey of Monmouth combined these in one character, but altered the name Myrddin to Merlin.[2] He also introduces Aurelius Ambrosius as a secondary character for whom Merlin creates Stonehenge as a burial place after he is poisoned.

The Merlin character is central to the story of Arthur as it is Merlin who is ultimately responsible for Arthur's birth. Uther Pendragon – brother to Aurelius who had become king after defeating Vortigern – had become obsessed with Igerna, the wife of Gorlois, Duke of Cornwall, and Merlin transforms his appearance so that Uther can enter Tintagel Castle. There he and Igerna conceive Arthur. Gorlois, besieged elsewhere by Uther's army, is killed that same night, allowing Uther and Igerna to marry, thus legitimizing the birth and allowing Arthur to become heir to the kingdom when Uther dies.

Arthur defeats the Saxons in a series of decisive battles, conquers Scotland, marries Guanhumara, of noble Roman descent but raised in Cornwall, before setting off to conquer Ireland, Iceland and other North Atlantic islands. With knights coming from far and wide to join his court over the next twelve years of peace, Arthur is able to conquer Norway, Denmark and Gaul. After such a major series of successes and nine years of battle, Arthur decides to hold a magnificent party at Caerleon, the City of Legions.

His success in Gaul – at that time under the rule of Rome – provokes a letter from emperor Lucius Tiberius[3] demanding he pays Rome tribute. Arthur's response, after taking counsel, is to warn Rome that he is on his way to demand tribute of his own.

Placing his nephew Modred in charge at home, Arthur heads off to fight the Romans and wins a great battle; Lucius Tiberius is killed and Arthur is marching on Rome when he learns that Modred has claimed the crown of Britain for his own and (adulterously) married Guanhumara.

Returning to Britain, Arthur's army meets with Modred's army of Saxons, Irish, Scots and Picts. Modred is killed and Arthur, mortally wounded, is taken to the Isle of Avallon to be cured. Arthur passes on his crown to his kinsman Constantine in the year 542.

* * * * *

The story as related by Geoffrey of Monmouth lacks many of the episodes that have since become part of the Arthurian legend. His book was an immediate and widespread success and was circulated around Britain and translated on the Continent. A Normandy poet called Wace produced *Roman de Brut* in c.1155, a relatively close translation into Anglo-Norman, although he added various speeches, names, comments and one or two new features of his own. One was the round table which Arthur introduces to stop any squabbling between nobles over precedence at table. Wace also added a line to Arthur's death: "The Bretons still await him".

Converting Geoffrey of Monmouth's prose into poetry also had the effect of romanticising the story and it was not long before other verse romances were being composed in France. Marie de France's *Lanval* was a fairy story in which a prince at King Arthur's court is taken up by a fairy mistress. Chrétien de Troyes composed no less than five romances

Have at you, fellow!

between c.1160 and 1190: *Erec et Enide, Cligés, Le chevalier de la charrette* (about Lancelot), *Yvain, Le Chevalier au lion* and the unfinished *Perceval, Le conte del graal*. The latter marks the earliest appearance of the Fisher King and the quest to seek the Holy Grail; its sudden ending led other writers to pick up the story, a group of verses known as the Four Continuations.

Chrétien was also responsible for introducing the story of Lancelot and his affair with Guinevere and, in passing, the first mention of Camelot.

According to Chrétien, Lancelot was raised by a water fay; his early life was expanded upon by Ulrich von Zatzikhoven, a lay priest who discovered the French work in the luggage of Hugh de Morville, a hostage for Richard the Lionheart when he was imprisoned in 1192-94. It is believed that Von Zatzikhoven's work – *Lanzelet* – was written in 1193 or not long after. The author expands upon Lancelot's childhood and relates how he is taken by the Lady of the Lake and raised in her magical kingdom. *Perlesvaus*, a continuation of Chrétien's *Perceval* written some time between 1200 and 1210, establishes Lancelot as one of the knights who search for the Holy Grail.

The story of Sir Tristan may have begun is a Pictish legend but was popularly retold in French in two versions by Thomas of Britain and Béroul, both under the title *Tristan*. These were expanded by German poets: the former by Gottfried von Strassburg (*Tristan*) and the latter by Eilhart von Oberge (*Tristrant*).

The affair between Tristan (or Tristram) and Iseult (or Isolde) – almost certainly an influence on the romance between Lancelot and Guinevere – was retold in the *Tristan en prose* (c.1240), which was more overtly Arthurian. Tristan joins the Knights of the Round Table and embarks on his own quest for the Holy Grail, an interpolation based on the *Queste del Saint Graal* from the Vulgate Cycle.

Earlier, French poet Robert de Boron had penned *Joseph d'Arimathe* (c.1200), which relates how Joseph of Armathea attracted a company of followers who take the Holy Grail to Britain. The search for the Grail forms the major part of the Vulgate Cycle, a series of anonymous linked prose stories, partly based on Robert de Boron's verses. The first three (c.1210) mostly concerned Lancelot and the Grail (*Lancelot propre and Queste del Saint Graal*) and the death of Arthur (*Mort Artu*); the series was added to in the 1230s with *Estoire del Sain Graal* and *Estoire de Merlin,* the latter relating the story of Merlin and the early adventures of Arthur which was subsequently expanded upon in *Suite de Merlin*.

The Vulgate Cycle brought together the various Arthurian stories and added greatly to them, introducing the sword in the stone, a test to establish Arthur's fitness to rule, revealing how Arthur obtained Excalibur from the Lady of the Lake and how the sword was returned to the lake, and how Arthur has unwitting incest with his half-sister Morgause and sires Mordred (as his name was by then more commonly known).

The most famous of all Arthurian works was another attempt to bring together a comprehensive collection of Arthurian tales. Its author, Sir Thomas Malory (c.1415-1471), was a justice of the peace, an MP elected five times, and was knighted in 1441. In 1450, he and a group of men attempted to ambush the Duke of Buckingham and over the next 18 months he was accused of extortion, theft, rape, cattle rustling, robbery and criminal damage. Over the next few years he was in and out of jail – sometimes bailed, sometimes escaping – before being pardoned. In 1468 he was again jailed, probably in the Tower of London, without formal charge for plotting against the new king, Edward IV. Although freed by the Lancastrians in 1470, he died soon after.

Written whilst in jail, Malory's manuscript was entitled *The hoole booke of kyng Arthur & of his noble knyghtes of the rounde table*. When it was finally printed in 1485 by William Caxton, it was erroneously given the title of the final section, *Le Morte Darthur*. Much of the work was based on Geoffrey of Monmouth's *Historia Brittonum* and the later *Vita Merlini* (in which Geoffrey reveals Merlin's later life and introduces Morgan Le Fey amongst others to the Arthurian legends) and the Vulgarian Cycle. Although Malory added little of his own, he did influence all future retellings of the story of Arthur. "Malory made his story one of the rise and fall of a great king and his kingdom," says P. J. C. Field.[4] "The symbolic power provided by this, by the innumerable quests and adventures contained in the book, and by the half-strange, half-familiar world of chivalric romance, reinforced by a transparent colloquial style that made events seem to stand free of any controlling author, quickly made it popular … In the next two centuries different tastes meant that the few readers interested in the 'matter of Britain' mostly looked to Geoffrey of Monmouth; but nineteenth-century medievalism raised the status of Malory's book to previously unimagined heights: Dante Gabriel Rossetti put it second only to the Bible. The twentieth century has seen it less admired but perhaps even more influential, affecting the media of films, cartoons, and computer games as well as established literary genres."

Down the centuries, the Arthurian legends have been revived many times. Alfred Tennyson's 'Morte d'Arthur' (1842) and Edward Bulwer-Lytton's 'King Arthur' (1848) helped raise their profile in the nineteenth century; J. T. Knowles retold Malory's work for boys in *The Story of King Arthur and his Knights of the Round Table* (1862) and Mark Twain satirized the legend in *A Connecticut Yankee at the Court of King Arthur* (1889).

Of the hundreds of stories that have included elements of the Arthurian legends, the most popular is possibly *The Once and Future King*, a cycle of five novels (1938-77)by T. H. White, the first of which – *The Sword in the Stone* – was adapted by Walt Disney in 1963. *King Arthur and his Knights of the Round Table* (1953) by Roger Lancelyn Green is probably the finest modern retelling.

* * * * *

The romances woven around King Arthur have created rather than elaborated on the life of a true Arthur. Little evidence exists for any person of that name (or some name from which Arthur could be derived) being the King of Britain. There may have been an Arthur, but the CVs of the legendary and the historical figures diverge immediately below his name.

The earliest mention of Arthur in surviving records would appear to be from the *Gododdin*, an elegiac poem from Scotland relating the fates of many warriors who fell in battles fighting the Angles at Catraeth. It is generally agreed by scholars that the battle took place around 600 and, after several days of fierce fighting, only three of the original 363 warriors survived. Towards the end of the many verses there is a stanza in which a warrior named Gwawrddur is mentioned who "brought black crows to a fort's / Wall, though he was not Arthur."[5]

Arguments still rage about the date this was originally composed – some argue it dates back to as early as 570 whilst others believe it was from as late as the 9th or even 10th century. The only surviving version is from the *Llyfr Aneirin*, or *Book of Aneirin*, which dates from the late 13th century.

Another early mention of Arthur comes from the *Elegy for Geraint*, which tells the story of an ancient battle at Llongborth: "In Llongborth I saw Arthur / And brave men who heed down with steel / Emperor, and conductor of the toll."[6] Again, it is impossible to date the battle with any accuracy as it has been argued that it relates to a battle at Portsmouth which the *Anglo-Saxon Chronicles* date as 501 or perhaps to the 8th century King Geraint of Dumnonia. As with *Y Gododdin*, the existing versions of the poem date from the 13th century.

The earliest source that can be accurately dated is the *Historia Brittonum*, previously mentioned as a major source for Geoffrey of Monmouth's *Historia Regum Britanniae*. This is believed to have been composed in c.829-830 by Nennius, a "disciple of St. Elbotus"[7] as he describes himself, who cheerfully admits that he has heaped together his history from various sources. Of most interest to Arthurian scholars is his chapter 50 and chapter 56 (almost a repeat of the former) in which Arthur, described as a military commander (*dux bellorum*), is attributed with fighting twelve major battles against the Saxons:

At that time, the Saxons grew strong by virtue of their large number and increased in power in Britain. Hengist having died, however, his son Octha crossed from the northern part of Britain to the kingdom of Kent and from him are descended the kings of Kent. Then Arthur along with the kings of Britain fought against them in those days, but Arthur himself was the military commander. His first battle was at the mouth of the river which is called Glein. His second, third, fourth, and fifth battles were above another river which is called Dubglas and is in the region of Linnuis. The sixth battle was above the river which is called Bassas. The seventh battle was in the forest of Celidon, that is Cat Coit Celidon. The eighth battle was at the fortress of Guinnion, in which Arthur carried the image of holy Mary ever virgin on his shoulders; and the pagans were put to flight on that day. And through the power of our Lord Jesus Christ and through the power of the blessed Virgin Mary his mother there was great slaughter among them. The ninth battle was waged in the City of the Legion. The tenth battle was waged on the banks of a river which is called Tribruit. The eleventh battle was fought on the mountain which is called Agnet. The twelfth battle was on Mount Badon in which there fell in one day 960 men from one charge by Arthur; and no one struck them down except Arthur himself, and in all the wars he emerged as victor. And while they were being defeated in all the battles, they were seeking assistance from Germany and their numbers were being augmented many times over without interruption. And they brought over kings from Germany that they might reign over them in Britain, right down to the time in which Ida reigned, who was son of Eobba. He was the first king in Bernicia, i.e., in Berneich.[8]

Of these the battle of Mount Badon (*Mons Badonicus*) is also mentioned in Gildas' *De Excidio et Conquestu Britanniae* – indeed, Gildas notes that it was fought in the year of his birth.[9] It is identified by Geoffrey of Monmouth as being Solsbury Hill, near Bath, although other locations have been suggested. Given the astonishing feat credited to Arthur by Nennius, one wonders why Gildas didn't name Arthur in his study of conquests and it has been argued that although Gildas is independent proof that a battle took place, he is also proof that Arthur, if he existed, had no connection with the battle. Indeed, Gildas seems to imply that the leader at Badon was Ambrosius Aurelianus, whom he specifically names as leading the first successful attacks against the Saxons. Ambrosius Aurelianus appears in Geoffrey of Monmouth's works under the slightly altered name of Aurelius Ambrosius and is thought to have been partly the inspiration for Merlin.

The Annales Cambriae (also known as *The Annals of Wales* and the *Historical Miscellany*) exist in four principal versions, one of which

appears in a 13th century MS of the *Historia Brittonum* but which appears to be from the late 10th century. The documents are calculations of the dates when Easter falls and were known as Easter Tables. They would have been copied numerous times, but it is generally presumed that events noted in previous versions would also be copied over. As they date events from the first table, it is in year 72 that the Battle of Badon is noted "in which Arthur carried the cross of our Lord Jesus Christ on his shoulders for three days and three nights and the Britons were victors". In Year 93, "The strife of Camlann in which Arthur and Mordred perished. And there was plague in Britain and Ireland". The latter note is missing from some versions of the documents and the similarity in wording between the comment for year 72 and the description by Nennius for Arthur's eighth battle at the fortress of Guinnion ("in which Arthur carried the image of holy Mary ever virgin on his shoulders; and the pagans were put to flight on that day") seems to make it clear that the comment was inspired by Nennius.

The date of these documents is debated but the general consensus is that year 72 would be around 516-18 and year 93 around 537-39.

No clear picture of Arthur emerges from these historical records: all dates are tentative and locations are open to wide interpretation, placing Arthur everywhere from Cornwall to Southern Scotland at various times. O. J. Padel neatly sums up the situation when he says: "The generally received view of the historical Arthur today is that he was probably a sixth-century battle leader of the British against the English, as portrayed in the *Historia Brittonum* attributed to Nennius. This view relies on that source and the two references in the *Annales Cambriae*, records composed three to four centuries later. But the *Historia Brittonum* also contains a contrasting portrayal of Arthur as a giant-like figure of legendary folklore. It is a matter of taste how one views this contrast in the earliest Arthurian document. It may show a historical Arthur already turning into a figure of legend, or a legendary Arthur becoming historicized. The weight of early evidence, and the absence of his name in Gildas, both favour the latter idea."[10]

* * * * *

If there was a historical figure at the back of Arthurian legend, he is barely discernable by the time we reach the early 1950s and the tale of 'King Arthur and his Knights' as it appeared in *Swift*. The story was told in 41 episodes between 30 July 1955 and 5 May 1956 and immediately followed a 41 week adaptation of Johann Wyss' classic novel *Swiss Family Robinson* (9 October 1954 to 16 July 1955).

The King Arthur story was scripted by Clifford Makins, who had become the sub-editor of the then newly launched *Swift* in 1954 when he accepted a position as personal assistant to editor Marcus Morris. He had met Morris, founder of the *Eagle* comic by chance and was, at the time, working in the accounts department of Faber & Faber and writing the occasional review for the *Times Literary Supplement*. Makins' background in theatre – he had been assistant stage manager for the Travelling Repertory Theatre founded by Basil C. Langton and later stage manager of the Ballet Negre – gave him a common interest with Morris, who was keen on film and theatre and had married an actress, Jessica Dunning.

How many stories Makins wrote for *Swift* is unknown but he was certainly fortunate to have Frank Bellamy as his artist for the strips he is known to have scripted. When Bellamy moved to *Eagle*, Makins was his scriptwriter for 'The Happy Warrior', 'The Shepherd King' and 'Montgomery of Alamein'… by which time good fortune presumably had nothing to do with it and editorial choice teamed writer and artist together.

Bellamy's work on King Arthur was a substantial improvement over his earlier adaptation of *Swiss Family Robinson*. The layout of the strip meant that, rather than ten cramped frames to a page, he now spread them over two pages, allowing a far more dramatic story to emerge. This was a swashbuckling strip in the style of swashbuckling movies and Bellamy's single frames across the width of the small tabloid-sized pages of *Swift*, gave the story the look of wide-screen cinema.

Bellamy made fine use of his wide-screen panels in some of the story's most dramatic moments: Arthur's escape – with the aid of Lancelot – from a ruined castle, the later attack on Lancelot's French stronghold and the jousting scenes between Lancelot and various knights. They were all given the space they deserved in the comic equivalent of Cinemascope.

The story dips into the Arthurian legends but retells only a fraction of the saga. We have the episodes of the sword in the stone and the Lady in the Lake, the Round Table, plus a few lesser-remembered elements such as the battle with King Lot at Sherwood Forest. After that, the story concentrates on intrigues within Camelot – with Mordred almost a comedy villain for the piece, complete with handlebar moustache – and the split between Arthur and Lancelot following a failed assassination attempt (by Mordred) against Arthur. The scene is set for some thrilling action as Arthur, convinced that Lancelot is his enemy, takes his army of Knights of the Round Table to France to attack those loyal to Lancelot. Meanwhile, Mordred is left in charge of Camelot, Merlin is imprisoned and his only hope is that Sir Kay will reach France to warn Arthur.

The look of the strip is very much in the tradition of how King Arthur and his knights have been portrayed in the past. By the time of the Vulgate Cycle, which brought together all the main elements of the Arthurian legends for the first time, the illuminated manuscript was also established and a romance such as that of King Arthur was often richly illustrated. Since there was no description of Arthur and no reference for French illuminators to work from, the images they created were of then-contemporary fashion, resplendent with heraldic symbols, and colourful imagery of Arthur and his court. Thus, although King Arthur was supposedly active in the dark ages, his image dates from the late medieval age.

The story is one of friendship and loyalty tested to their very limits. The hero of the story is really Sir Lancelot: when he is tested he is found to be brave, loyal and a true knight. Lancelot is, however, already a knight when he is first introduced. Arthur, on the other hand, is still young and has to learn the chivalric code. Whether he lives up to what is expected of him as the chosen King of Britain you will be able to discover for yourself in the following pages.

Steve Holland, Colchester, 2008

1   Geoffrey of Monmouth was influential in persuading his friend, Caradoc of Llancarfan, to write a biography of Gildas.
2   It was suggested by French scholar Gaston Paris that the change was made to avoid any association of Myrddin with the French work merde.
3   Lucius Tiberius was a fictional character created by Geoffrey of Monmouth. No emperor of this name exists in Roman history.
4   P. J. C. Field, 'Sir Thomas Malory', Oxford Dictionary of National Biography, Oxford University Press, Sept 2004; online edn., Jan 2008 (accessed 7 July 2008).
5   From the translation of Joseph P. Clancey, London & New York, Macmillan, 1970.
6   From the translation of William F. Skene, Edinburgh, Edmonston & Douglas, 1868.
7   St. Elbotus, or Elvodugus, is thought to be the Welsh bishop Elfoddw of Gwynedd (d. 809).
8   From the translation of Alan Lupack, http://www.fordham.edu/halsall/source/nennius.html (accessed 7 July 2008).
9   In its most widely available translation by J. A. Giles, Mons Badonicus becomes Bath-hill and the battle raged "forty-four years and one month after the landing of the Saxons, and also the time of my own nativity". Gildas' birth is variously dated c.498, c.504 or 516.
10 O. J. Padel, 'King Arthur', Oxford Dictionary of National Biography, Oxford University Press, Sept 2004; online edn., Jan 2008 (accessed 7 July 2008).

FRANK BELLAMY'S

KING ARTHUR
AND HIS KNIGHTS

FRANK BELLAMY

King Arthur and his Knights

When King Uther of Britain died there was no heir to the throne and the lords fought among themselves. The people longed for a King to rule over them.

One day Sir Ector, an old knight who had been the King's friend, came home to his castle near London with some exciting news from the city.

Had a good trip, Father?

Come inside. I'll tell you all about it.

Sir Ector was greeted by his son, Sir Kay, who had just been knighted, and his adopted son, Arthur, a quiet boy whom no-one noticed very much.

There is a great stone and on the stone is an anvil, and stuck in the anvil is a marvellous sword!

The old knight told the boys a strange story. Overnight in a churchyard in the City of London, a great stone had appeared with a bright sword thrust into it.

No-one knows. No-one can pull it from the stone!

Is it a heavy sword?

Eagerly Sir Kay questioned his father about the strange sword. Arthur listened intently by the fireside but said nothing at all.

It says on the sword that whoever draws it from the stone is King of Britain.

Oh! I must try!

Sir Ector told the boys of the writing on the blade of the sword. Sir Kay was keen to try his luck and his father agreed that they should all go to London.

Later that night, as Sir Kay and Arthur were going to bed, they were still thinking of the sword in the stone. Sir Kay especially was very excited.

Alone in his room, Arthur found it difficult to sleep. As soon as the sword had been mentioned by Sir Kay, Arthur had felt a strange feeling of power.

The story of the sword became known all over Britain. Many lords and knights came to London. Each one hoped to win the throne for himself.

Sir Ector, Sir Kay and Arthur rode to the churchyard which was crowded with people. Arthur longed for a chance to draw the sword from the stone.

By the time Sir Ector and the boys arrived on the scene the crowd were growing impatient. Many lords and knights had tried to take the sword but all had failed to move it. As the crowd laughed and jeered Arthur felt a wonderful power within him which he could not explain.

Sir Kay and his brother, Arthur, had travelled to London to see the sword in the stone. The man who drew the sword would be made King of Britain.

In the great churchyard the crowd buzzed with excitement. No-one had succeeded in drawing the sword from the stone. Then Sir Kay stepped forward.

Sir Kay tugged at the sword with all his might but it stayed in the stone. The lords and knights were growing impatient. They felt they had been tricked.

Arthur stepped forward and spoke to the Archbishop and the wise old man Merlin. When he said he could take out the sword, a hush fell upon the people.

The silence was broken by the Archbishop, who was astonished, and by the unpleasant King Lot. The old man Merlin said Arthur should be given a chance.

Arthur grasped the sword and gave it a light, fierce pull. With the greatest of ease the sword left the stone, and Arthur held it triumphantly.

Arthur stood still. The churchyard echoed with the chatter of the people. They were astounded that he had succeeded where powerful lords had failed.

Merlin proclaimed Arthur as King of Britain. King Lot, who wanted the throne for himself, cried out that the other kings and lords would not accept Arthur.

Arthur stood his ground and cried out to the crowd that he was their King. The people cheered. They were on Arthur's side, and King Lot's protests were in vain.

After a while, Arthur went into the church where he was to be made a knight and then crowned King of Britain. It was the greatest day of his life.

After his Coronation King Arthur sat in the great church while the knights and lords came forward to swear to serve him faithfully. Arthur made his first act as King when he chose Sir Kay as his steward. The great and exciting story of King Arthur and his Knights had begun!

11

King Arthur and his Knights

Arthur had drawn the sword from the stone and was proclaimed King of Britain. The news caused great rejoicing and amazement throughout the land.

King Arthur went to the great castle at Camelot where he lived throughout his reign. One autumn morning he rode from the castle with Merlin.

'After a short gallop, King Arthur and Merlin rode slowly through the forest. They talked of the jealous lords and rebel kings who were still envious of Arthur.

Arthur and Merlin were deep in conversation and did not notice the armed knight watching them from the top of the hill. His horse and armour were black.

Suddenly the ground shook. Arthur and Merlin looked up. The black knight galloped down the hill-side at full speed. Merlin shouted a warning to Arthur.

A few moments later the knight reached King Arthur and Merlin and reined in his horse, blocking their path. Deliberately he insulted King Arthur to his face.

Arthur kept calm but his hand went to his sword. He looked at the fearless face of the knight and knew that he would have to fight for his life.

The rebel knight went back, then wheeled his horse around and prepared to charge on Arthur. The knight was heavily armoured and carried a huge lance.

The knight charged at full speed and thrust the lance at the King's heart, but Arthur was quick with his shield and forced the lance from the knight's grasp.

In a flash Arthur raised his sword and struck the knight a mighty blow. The knight was knocked from his horse, but to Arthur's horror his sword broke.

The fallen knight paid homage to the young king but Arthur was distressed. He had won his first fight but the sword from the stone was broken.

And then the knight told Arthur that if he rode on he would come to a lake and find another sword there. Arthur was amazed but he believed the knight.

King Arthur was out riding with his wise old counsellor, Merlin, when he was challenged by a knight. Arthur won the fight but broke his sword.

King Arthur and Merlin rode on to a lake. The defeated knight had told Arthur that he would find another sword that would last the King all his life.

Arthur and Merlin walked round the lake looking for the sword but all they found was a boat. Suddenly Merlin cried out and pointed across the water.

In the middle of the lake they saw a hand appearing out of the waters. The hand was grasping a sword in a scabbard which shone brightly through the mist.

King Arthur and Merlin jumped into the boat. The young King pulled heavily on the oars and the boat leapt through the water towards the sword.

King Arthur leaned from the boat and grasped the sword. The hand, which had held the sword above the water slowly vanished beneath the surface of the lake.

Arthur sat in the boat examining the sword he had taken from the water. It was a magnificent sword and the word 'Excalibur' was engraved on its blade.

King Arthur and Merlin returned to the castle. At the gate they met Sir Kay and Arthur told him about the sword he had found in the lake.

They walked on the battlements and Arthur admired his new sword. Sir Kay told Arthur that King Lot was gathering a huge army near Sherwood Forest.

King Arthur looked out from his castle over the country he had begun to rule. He decided to march against the rebel King Lot to fight for his kingdom.

A few days later, on a bright moonlit night, King Arthur and his army reached the great forest of Sherwood. In the cool evening air King Arthur stood with Sir Kay beneath the trees. In the distance he saw the camp fires of King Lot's armies. He decided to attack in the morning. *More next week.*

15

King Arthur had led a big army to Sherwood Forest. He was about to fight the rebel King Lot who was jealous of Arthur and wanted the throne for himself.

King Arthur was ready to attack King Lot's army. The old knight, Sir Ector, thought it was a bad idea to attack first, but Arthur had made up his mind.

Arthur mounted his horse as Merlin stood by. For the first time he was going to lead his army into battle. Everything depended on his skill and courage.

Arthur was mounted on his horse with his great sword Excalibur by his side. A soldier sounded the charge on a horn and shattered the silence around them.

The great moment was at hand. From the fringe of Sherwood Forest a long line of mounted knights galloped in bright sunshine across the flat fields. At

the head of the knights, lance in hand, was Arthur the young King of Britain! They swept on, faster and faster, towards the waiting army of the rebel King Lot.

As King Arthur and his knights galloped over the plain King Lot watched the advance and jeered at Arthur's sudden charge. He felt sure of victory.

King Lot's archers knelt down some distance from the charging horses. Suddenly a hail of arrows rained down on King Arthur's knights. The battle had begun!

The battle raged for some time. Then Arthur left his steward, Sir Kay, and galloped off in search of the rebel King Lot to challenge him to fight.

King Arthur quickly found the rebel King who had already defeated several knights. Arthur reined in his horse and issued a ringing challenge.

But as Arthur called on King Lot to fight with him, a foot soldier crept up from behind. With one good blow he struck King Arthur from his horse.

King Arthur was up in a flash and drew his sword. King Lot, heavily armed, galloped towards Arthur with a cry of triumph.

King Arthur and his Knights

King Arthur took his Army to Sherwood Forest to fight the rebel King Lot. As Arthur was about to fight him, he was knocked from his saddle.

The rebel King Lot urged his mount forward and rode full tilt at Arthur who kept quite still and did not flinch. The huge horse pounded towards him.

From the saddle of his galloping horse King Lot thrust his lance at Arthur who stepped aside just in time. The lance bit deep into the earth.

King Lot's powerful charge carried him past King Arthur. At that moment Arthur's horse came trotting forward. Arthur ran to seize the reins.

He had to mount his horse before King Lot made another attack, but as he clutched at the reins the horse galloped off. Arthur had lost his chance.

And then King Lot turned in the distance and began another attack. Arthur, full of courage, took the great lance from the earth to defend himself.

King Lot charged and Arthur struck him on the breastplate with the lance. King Lot swayed in his saddle but kept his seat and did not fall.

King Lot fell forward on the neck of his horse which galloped away. Arthur could see that King Lot was hurt and unable to hold the reins.

The wounded King Lot rode away in the distance and Arthur's steward, Sir Kay, appeared. He was leading King Arthur's horse.

Without delay King Arthur mounted his horse. His Army was still fighting and King Lot, though wounded, was still mounted. The battle was not over yet.

King Arthur with Sir Kay, at the head of his knights, pursued King Lot and found him together with the lords and captains who had survived the battle. The rebel King was making light of his wounds. Arthur admired his courage. If King Lot was prepared to fight on, it would be a bitter battle! *More Next Week*.

King Arthur and his Knights

King Arthur was fighting King Lot near Sherwood Forest. The battle was nearly over and Arthur's Army was winning, but King Lot was still defiant.

In a corner of the battlefield King Lot had collected a group of his lords who were all ready to defend themselves against King Arthur's Army.

The battlefield was quiet. King Lot and his lords were surrounded. Sir Kay was full of triumph but King Arthur did not wish to take revenge upon them.

King Arthur was now sure of victory and the lives of King Lot and his lords were in his hands. King Arthur then decided to pardon the rebels.

Supported by one of his lords, the wounded King Lot went over to Arthur and pledged his faith and his honour to the King. It was the end of the day and the

end of the battle. The young King Arthur had proved himself a great soldier and everyone in the field admired his skill and tremendous courage.

Three days later King Arthur and Sir Kay galloped up the drawbridge of Arthur's castle at Camelot. They had ridden hard and left the Army far behind.

In the castle courtyard King Arthur and Sir Kay got down from their horses. As they did so the wise old Merlin rode slowly into the courtyard.

Old Merlin was pleased with the beginning made by the young man he had proclaimed King. He was very proud of Arthur's courage on the battlefield.

The young King and his old counsellor walked through the castle. Merlin told Arthur that Excalibur was a sword which would protect him always.

At last they came to the great hall of the castle. Arthur was sad that the splendid room was dark and empty. And then old Merlin spoke of the many knights who would serve the King and of the great Round Table at which the King would hold his Court. Arthur was thrilled. *More Next Week.*

King Arthur and his Knights

After his defeat of King Lot, Arthur returned to Camelot. Merlin told him that he should hold court there and build a great Round Table for his knights.

From the counties all over Britain and from France and Spain a great host of noble knights came to join the court of the young King Arthur.

The King is well supported, Mordred!

Yes! — for the time being!

Today the Knights of the Round Table will come into being..... what great adventures lie ahead for all of us!

But amongst this company of splendid knights Arthur had two secret enemies, Sir Mordred and Sir Agravain. They were both related to the young King.

Helped by his page, King Arthur put on his most magnificent suit of armour. Very soon he would greet the great host of knights who had come from afar.

Sire, your knights are waiting in the great hall.

I am ready, Sir Kay.

Sound the trumpets for Arthur, King of Britain!

As the page handed King Arthur the crown Sir Kay came into the room. He had come to escort the King to the great hall where the knights were.

As King Arthur came to the great doors of the hall his steward, Sir Kay, called out for the trumpets to sound, and everyone knew the King was coming.

The sunlight poured through the windows into the great hall. King Arthur, wearing his magnificent armour and splendid crown, took his place at the centre of the mighty Round Table where he was to hold his court for many years to come. The men who had come to serve him all shouted for joy.

The company of knights sat at the Round Table. They listened with intense excitement as Arthur told them of the wonderful adventures they would undertake.

After the first meeting of the Round Table, Arthur walked in the courtyard. Suddenly his page ran up with news of a stranger who rode on a white horse.

King Arthur ordered the castle gates to be opened. As the drawbridge was lowered the man on the white horse spurred his mount forward to the drawbridge.

King Arthur met the man at the gates of the castle. It was Lancelot who was destined to be the King's best and bravest knight. *More Next Week.*

King Arthur and his Knights

King Arthur held a meeting of his knights at the great Round Table in the castle hall. Afterwards a man on a white horse rode into the courtyard.

King Arthur welcomed Lancelot to his court and made him a knight. Arthur and Lancelot soon became friends and often went out riding together.

As the King and Sir Lancelot rode in the morning sunshine they were watched by Sir Mordred, who had falsely sworn himself to be a true knight.

Sir Mordred and Sir Agravaine rode to a forest glade where a gang of ruffians waited. Mordred told them to hide in the forest and to wait for the King.

The ruffians hid themselves. The two false knights, Sir Mordred and Sir Agravaine, were pleased with the trap. They prepared to gallop back to the castle.

Arthur and Lancelot rode through the forest unaware of the men who lurked in the bushes. The ruffians waited impatiently, ready to attack.

King Arthur and Sir Lancelot rode peacefully into the ambush Mordred had laid for them. The ruffians sprang out from their hiding places and dragged Arthur and Lancelot from their horses. The King and his knight were heavily outnumbered and had no time to draw their swords, but each struggled fiercely.

King Arthur and Sir Lancelot fought like tigers but the odds against them were very great. The full weight of the attack was directed at the King and before long he was overpowered and hustled away into the forest. Meanwhile Lancelot fought on, giving blow for blow! He was determined to fight to the end for his King.

The King's captors rushed him through the forest to a river where a long barge was moored to the bank. King Arthur was forced into the barge.

The barge was rowed swiftly down the river. King Arthur was a prisoner – bound and helpless! Would Lancelot be able to rescue him? *More Next Week*.

King Arthur and his Knights

King Arthur and Sir Lancelot were ambushed while riding in the forest. Arthur was made prisoner and rushed to the river where he was taken away in a barge.

Meanwhile, Sir Lancelot fought on in the forest. His strength and agility surprised his attackers. He beat them off and sent them reeling with his blows.

Sir Lancelot broke away, ran to his horse, seized the reins, and leapt into the saddle. The ruffians were hot on his heels. There was no time to lose!

Back in the saddle again Sir Lancelot rode his horse straight at the ruffians. They jumped for their lives as the knight thundered past. Sir Lancelot had escaped!

Sir Lancelot was bruised and sore after his hard fight but he gave no thought to himself as he galloped through the forest. He had to rescue the King.

Very soon Sir Lancelot reached the river bank. In the distance he could see the barge gliding downstream and at once he decided to follow it.

Some time later the barge came to an old ruined castle which stood on the river bank. The castle looked cold and empty as if no-one had lived there for many years. The King's captors laughed and jeered, but Arthur showed no sign of fear. He sat in the barge with his arms bound and waited patiently.

King Arthur was taken ashore and led to the gate of the old ruined castle. On the steps he was met by a villainous-looking man who was the gaoler.

The King was taken to a cell in the castle and his arms untied. He asked the gaoler who had ordered his capture but the man refused to tell him.

Alone in his prison Arthur thought of the strange events which had taken place. Who was behind the plot to capture him? And where was Lancelot?

The brave knight, Sir Lancelot, looked across the water at the walls of the castle. He felt sure he was on the track of the King! *More next week.*

King Arthur and his Knights

King Arthur had been captured by ruffians at the order of the false knight Mordred. The King was shut up in a ruined castle but Lancelot was close at hand.

Just beyond the castle Sir Lancelot found a small bridge over a stream. He tied his horse to a tree and walked lightly over the narrow bridge.

Lancelot crouched in the long grass in front of the castle in the moonlight. He decided to climb the wall and hope for the best. He had to rescue the King!

The great wall of the castle had many cracks and footholds, but Sir Lancelot climbed very slowly for fear of making a noise. There was no sign of a guard.

In the castle hall the gaoler slept before the fire. Behind him the door opened and Sir Lancelot crept in silently with his dagger drawn.

The gaoler awoke from his dreams to find Sir Lancelot's dagger at his throat. Sir Lancelot spoke in a whisper but he was in a very determined mood!

King Arthur was sitting on his bench in the cell when the door opened. The gaoler came in followed by Lancelot. Arthur cried out with surprise and joy. But the King was not out of danger yet. Lancelot knew that they must hurry if they were to escape from the castle with their lives.

Without a moment's delay King Arthur and Sir Lancelot left the cell, locking the gaoler in behind them. Arthur drew his sword, Excalibur.

Arthur and Lancelot hurried along the corridor to the stairway which was the only way of escape. The moonlight threw their shadows on to the floor.

Arthur and Lancelot ran down the stairway. Another moment and they would have been out of the castle. Then, out of the shadows, from behind and in front of them, sprang four men armed with deadly weapons. The King and his knight stood trapped on the steep staircase! *More Next Week*

King Arthur and his Knights

Lancelot broke into a ruined castle where King Arthur was a prisoner. He set the King free, but as they were leaving the castle they were trapped.

King Arthur and Lancelot were faced with certain death if they did not act quickly. They sprang forward, determined to fight their way out of the castle.

One ruffian thrust at Arthur with his pike. With one great stroke Arthur sliced the pike in two and cried out the name of his sword in triumph!

The King and Sir Lancelot were in great fighting mood and the two men with pikes were quickly knocked aside. Arthur called to Lancelot.

The pikemen were beaten and Arthur and Lancelot ran to the big door which led to the castle court-yard. They were pursued by the two ruffians from

the top of the stairway. As Lancelot put his hand on the door a great battle-axe whistled through the air and bit deep into the wood behind the King!

Bursting from the castle hall, King Arthur and Sir Lancelot ran across the court-yard and swarmed up the wall. They could be easily seen in the bright moonlight and a hail of arrows came after them. King Arthur was first up the wall and he reached down to give Sir Lancelot a helping hand.

Arthur and Lancelot jumped safely on the other side of the castle wall. They had to cross the river by the narrow bridge which led to the castle.

They crossed the bridge and found Lancelot's horse. There wasn't a moment to lose and as soon as Lancelot was in the saddle the King leapt up.

It was a strange sight to see King Arthur riding behind one of his knights! After a hard gallop, they left their pursuers far behind.

It was early morning when they reached Camelot. Arthur was very thoughtful. He longed to find out who was his enemy. *More next week.*

31

King Arthur and his Knights

Sir Lancelot rescued King Arthur from the castle where he was held prisoner. Meanwhile, Sir Mordred was at Camelot, not knowing of the King's escape.

You're up early, Mordred!

Hurry up! We have a lot to do!

As King Arthur and Sir Lancelot approached Camelot, Sir Mordred, the false knight, was already up and paying a call on Sir Agravaine, his henchman.

Arthur and Lancelot are prisoners. No one will find them. We will seize power and rule the country!

Sir Mordred was very pleased with himself. He was confident that King Arthur and Sir Lancelot were prisoners. He could now make himself King.

There is old Merlin and Sir Kay!

They are still waiting for the King! What a hope!

Mordred and Agravaine looked out on to the battlements. The King's counsellor, Merlin, and the King's steward, Sir Kay, were watching.

I fear the worst for King Arthur...

Merlin! Look! Look there!

On the castle battlements Merlin and Sir Kay walked up and down. Merlin was feeling gloomy about the King when Sir Kay suddenly cried out in excitement.

The King!

He's waving to us! And Lancelot's with him! They're safe!

In the distance King Arthur and Sir Lancelot approached the castle on foot. Sir Kay and Merlin both shouted for joy. The King was alive and well!

When a page told Mordred and Agravaine that the King had arrived, the two false knights were amazed. They just couldn't believe their ears!

From a corner of the court-yard the two false knights watched Arthur and Lancelot being greeted. Sir Mordred was furious that his plot had failed.

After Merlin had heard of Arthur's adventures he told the King to rest. But Arthur was determined to ride back to the castle where he had been imprisoned.

Before long the King was on the move again. At the head of his knights he galloped from Camelot back to the ruined castle to find his captors.

King Arthur and his knights rode at full speed until they came to the river. The ruined castle was on fire. Flames licked the walls and clouds of smoke rose into the sky. All traces of Sir Mordred's plot were destroyed! Now King Arthur could not find out who had betrayed him. *More next week.*

33

Ring Arthur and his Rnights

With a troop of knights Arthur returned to the ruined castle where he had been held prisoner. When they arrived they found the castle on fire.

They crossed the river to the burning castle. Lancelot made a tour of the walls but there was no sign of the men who had imprisoned the King.

As the knights rode away from the burning castle Sir Kay told Arthur that he should have a body-guard but the King laughed at this suggestion.

King Arthur rode back to Camelot. At the rear the false knight, Sir Mordred, told Sir Argravaine of a new plot to cause the downfall of the King.

Back in the castle at Camelot, Mordred made sure that Lancelot was out of the way. Agravaine kept watch while Mordred went into Lancelot's room.

Mordred searched Lancelot's room and he soon found the dagger with Lancelot's crest on the hilt. He pounced on it with a cry of triumph.

Mordred and Agravaine got away unseen. The false knight was about to embark on his most evil plan – to kill Arthur with Lancelot's dagger!

As the two villains disappeared Arthur and Lancelot came on the scene. The King had just thanked Lancelot once again for saving his life.

Alone in his room, Arthur prepared to go to bed. He was thinking that Sir Lancelot should be rewarded for his splendid courage and loyalty to him.

King Arthur went to bed and soon was fast asleep. Just after midnight the door opened silently. Sir Mordred crept in, disguised in a hooded cloak.

The moonlight poured into the King's room. All was quiet except for the slight sound of Arthur's breathing and the light step of the hooded man as he crept towards the sleeping King with a dagger in his hand. The bright steel of the dagger flashed in the moonlight. *More next week.*

King Arthur and his Knights

Mordred creeps into King Arthur's bedroom disguised in a cloak. He is carrying Lancelot's dagger so that the suspicion will fall on him.

The hooded knight stood by Arthur's bed, ready to strike with his dagger. Suddenly the King woke up and saw the figure standing over him.

The hooded knight struck at Arthur with all his force. The King was hardly awake but he caught the knight's wrist strongly and held off the dagger.

King Arthur summoned all his strength. Still holding off the dagger, he raised himself on his bed and struck the hooded knight a blow on the head.

The hooded knight dropped the dagger and ran from the room. King Arthur jumped from his bed and his powerful voice rang through the castle.

King Arthur had not recognised his attacker. Mordred ripped off his hood and threw it out of the window. Then he raised the alarm.

Sir Kay, the King's steward, ran up to the cunning Mordred who pretended to be alarmed and upset. They hurried off to King Arthur's room.

Sir Kay and Mordred rushed into the King's room where they found the King with Merlin. Arthur looked very grave as he told them the news.

When Arthur mentioned the dagger, the crafty Mordred saw his chance. He looked at the dagger and told the King that it was Lancelot's!

There was an awful silence. When Arthur spoke he looked puzzled and sad. He did not believe that his friend Lancelot was the hooded knight.

Suddenly Sir Lancelot appeared. He had run from his room, sword in hand, when he heard the King's voice. He had come to defend Arthur and he stood astonished as the false knight Sir Mordred accused him of trying to kill the King. Will Lancelot be able to clear his name? *More next week.*

37

King Arthur and his Knights

Mordred, in disguise, tried to kill Arthur with Lancelot's dagger as he slept. But the King woke up. Mordred dropped the dagger and escaped.

Sir Kay, the King's steward, arrested Lancelot on suspicion of trying to kill the King. Sir Lancelot was astounded at the accusation.

Sir Lancelot was escorted from the room. Mordred was pleased. He had failed to kill the King but he had managed to put the blame on Lancelot.

Arthur felt troubled. He could not believe his faithful knight who had helped him so often had tried to kill him. Merlin felt sad too.

Sir Kay took Lancelot to his room and left him there. The brave knight, who only the day before had rescued the King, was now a prisoner.

Sir Lancelot could not sleep that night. He realised that someone within the castle was plotting against himself and the King to ruin their friendship.

Next day Sir Lancelot was taken to the great hall of the castle. At a meeting of the Knights of the Round Table he was found guilty of trying to kill the King. The hall rang with the cries of the angry knights. They demanded that Lancelot should die for his treachery. The King listened sadly.

There was silence as King Arthur stood up and gave his verdict on Sir Lancelot. He ruled that the knight should be driven from court.

In the court-yard Sir Lancelot prepared to mount his horse and ride off. He spoke earnestly to the King he had served and loved so well.

And so Sir Lancelot, the bravest of the Knights of the Round Table, rode from Camelot. Arthur was very sad. He had lost his best friend. But the wicked Mordred was delighted. With Lancelot out of the way he could now go ahead with his plan to seize the throne. *More next week.*

King Arthur and his Knights

The false knight Mordred tries to kill King Arthur with Lancelot's dagger. The suspicion falls on Lancelot, who is banished from Camelot for ever.

As Sir Lancelot rode out of sight he was watched from the castle by Mordred and the wicked Agravaine. Mordred had another evil plan.

Mordred knew that Lancelot was a brave knight who would always be loyal to King Arthur. He told Agravaine to follow Lancelot and kill him.

Agravaine galloped from Camelot Castle with three other knights who hated King Arthur. They thought Lancelot would be an easy victim.

Lancelot was riding to Cardiff, where he hoped to take a ship to his home in France. Not far from the city he stopped at an inn for a meal.

While Sir Lancelot was eating, Sir Agravaine and his men approached the inn. Suddenly they saw Lancelot's splendid white horse in the inn-yard!

The unhappy Sir Lancelot had just finished his meal and was deep in thought when the door burst open. There stood the boastful Sir Agravaine with his band of hostile knights. Their swords were drawn and they roared with delight because they had trapped the brave knight so easily!

There were four men against one. Yet Sir Lancelot, although surprised by the treacherous knights, fought with all his skill and cunning. With his left hand he seized a stool and struck down one of the knights. Then he lunged with his sword at their cowardly leader, Agravaine, and wounded him.

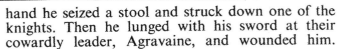

Two enemies remained. Sir Lancelot made for the window, fighting fiercely all the way. He had to use both his hands and feet to defend himself.

Turning sharply, Lancelot leapt through the window. The angry knights gasped as he plunged down into the inn-yard below. *More next week.*

King Arthur and his Knights

Sir Lancelot, wrongly banished from King Arthur's court, has been attacked by armed knights. After a fierce fight he escapes through the window of an inn.

Lancelot leapt safely to the ground and ran to his horse. The knights in the inn were amazed that Lancelot had slipped out of their clutches.

Sir Lancelot galloped away. The knight by the window urged his comrades to ride after Lancelot but they stood still beside the body of their leader,

Sir Agravaine. He was dead, killed by a sharp thrust of Lancelot's sword. They would have to return to Camelot and break the news to Mordred.

Safe from pursuit, Sir Lancelot rode at full speed until he came in sight of the city of Cardiff where he was hoping to board a ship for France.

Lancelot rode through the cobbled streets until he came to the waterside. With affection, he patted his tired and gallant horse on the neck.

And then, as he reached the sea and the ships, Sir Lancelot had a terrible shock. Standing on the quayside was another party of knights armed to the teeth! Even the brave Lancelot felt his courage sink at the sight of this band. Was he about to fall into another trap? He reined in his horse.

The leader of these knights was a gallant young man called Sir Lionel. Lancelot was astonished when he heard what Sir Lionel had to say to him!

Sir Lionel pointed to a ship which was about to set sail for France. The knights said they would go with Sir Lancelot to France and serve him.

The ship set sail. And so Sir Lancelot was honoured by a band of knights who had left Arthur's court for the sake of the bravest knight in Britain.

On deck, Lancelot thought of his friend Arthur. Would the King discover the enemies in his court before it was too late? *More next week.*

King Arthur and his Knights

Sir Lancelot, banished from King Arthur's court, has sailed to France with a band of knights who have chosen to serve him. Their leader is Sir Lionel.

King Arthur was walking on the castle's battlements when the old counsellor, Merlin, told him about the knights who had joined Lancelot.

King Arthur felt sad when he heard Merlin's news. Then he spied three men galloping furiously over the plain towards the castle. What had happened?

The three knights rode over the drawbridge with a great clatter. They reined in their horses and began calling for King Arthur and Sir Mordred.

In the court-yard the three men sat grimly on their horses. King Arthur, his steward, Sir Kay, and the old man, Merlin, listened gravely while the knights told them of the death of Agravaine. They told the story in such a way that it appeared that Lancelot had started the fight and was entirely to blame.

King Arthur's face clouded with anger. Now he had lost all his faith in Sir Lancelot and felt at last that his best friend was really his enemy.

King Arthur left the court-yard with his steward and his counsellor. Sir Mordred was highly delighted that the King was angry with Lancelot.

The King went to his room with Sir Kay. He was still very angry and ordered Merlin to call the Knights of the Round Table together for a meeting.

Sir Kay listened in silence as the angry Arthur cried out that he would pursue Lancelot to his home in France and challenge him to battle.

At a meeting of the Round Table it was decided that King Arthur and his Knights would follow Lancelot and cross the sea and give battle with him in France. Arthur left Mordred in charge of the Kingdom and the false knight's heart was full of glee. Now he could seize power! *More next week.*

King Arthur and his Knights

Sir Lancelot has sailed to France. King Arthur has decided to follow him and fight him. The false knight, Mordred, has been left in charge of the kingdom.

And so, one bleak day in autumn, King Arthur rode from the castle at the head of his Knights. His great sword, Excalibur, was by his side.

As the Knights of the Round Table left Camelot, the wicked Mordred spoke to his kinsman, Sir Gawaine, who also hated King Arthur and feared Lancelot.

The King's steward, Kay, and the old man Merlin saw Mordred whispering to Gawaine. They began to be suspicious of the evil knight, Mordred.

King Arthur and his Knights of the Round Table rode through the streets of Cardiff. News of their coming had spread throughout the town and the streets were lined with people who loved the King. They shouted and cheered and gazed in wonder at the King's splendid armour and his great sword.

In the harbour was a fleet of ships to take the King and his Knights to France. There were also foot-soldiers and archers and many others who formed a great army to make war on Lancelot. The King went on board his ship with Gawaine, and they watched the great stir and bustle on the quayside.

It was dark when the fleet set sail. Before he went to bed, the false knight, Gawaine, said goodnight to Arthur and spoke scornfully of Sir Lancelot.

As the ship rolled on the dark sea, Arthur lay in his bunk unable to sleep and once more his thoughts turned to Lancelot who had been his best friend.

Next morning Arthur was attended by his page, who dressed the King in warlike armour. The Captain rushed in and told the King land was in sight.

Sir Gawaine pointed to the coast and said that soon Lancelot would be afraid. The King said nothing – he knew how brave Lancelot was! *More next week.*

King Arthur and his knights are sailing to France in pursuit of the banished Lancelot. The wicked Mordred has been left in charge of the Kingdom.

The fleet of ships which carried King Arthur's army across the sea sailed close to the French coast. There was no sign of life on the shore.

But as King Arthur's fleet dropped anchor in the bay, two men were watching from the top of a cliff. They could see the decks swarming with knights

and soldiers who were getting ready to land. Lancelot's castle was not far from the sea. He had to be warned of the invasion at once!

Without a moment's delay, the messenger jumped on his horse and rode furiously across the flat fields to carry the news speedily to Sir Lancelot.

The messenger thundered through the gates of Lancelot's castle and the sweating horse reared in the air as his rider pulled sharply on the reins!

Sir Lancelot was sitting in his court room with Sir Lionel and a French knight when the messenger burst into the room. The man threw himself at the feet of Lancelot and blurted out the news of Arthur's landing. Sir Lionel jumped up in alarm – but Sir Lancelot kept still and said nothing.

When Lancelot spoke to Sir Lionel he sounded gloomy. He realised that Arthur had followed him to France with all the Knights of the Round Table.

Lionel pleaded with Lancelot to leave the castle with his soldiers and surprise Arthur's army, but the banished knight refused to start the battle.

Meanwhile, the King's army was heading towards Lancelot's castle. King Arthur sent scouts ahead. He was puzzled to learn that there was no sign of Lancelot's supporters anywhere. Will Lancelot keep his word – or will he be forced to fight with his friend, King Arthur? *More next week.*

King Arthur and his Knights

King Arthur and his army have landed in France and are advancing towards the castle of the banished Lancelot, who was once the King's best friend.

Beware of Lancelot, Sire. He may be laying a trap for us.

I don't think so.

King Arthur's army moved towards Lancelot's castle. There was no sign of Lancelot and his men and the crafty Sir Gawaine feared a trap.

Look! A great castle!

It must be Lancelot's castle. We must ride back to the King!

From the brow of a hill two of Arthur's knights, who were sent ahead, saw a great castle. Without a doubt this was the castle of the banished Lancelot!

We have sighted the castle, Sire!

I will go and challenge Lancelot to battle!

The two knights galloped back to the army and gave their news to the King. Arthur ordered his army to get ready to advance on Lancelot's castle!

It is a strong fortress, your Majesty!

We will break into the castle and burn it to the ground!

You are too rash, Gawaine. It will not be easy to defeat Lancelot!

A short while later King Arthur and his knights and the great army he had brought with him to France, rode across the plain towards Lancelot's castle.

Sir Gawaine, acting on the wicked Mordred's orders, urged Arthur to attack the castle in full force, but the King knew his own mind and refused!

King Arthur's army rode slowly towards the castle. From the battlements Lancelot was watching with Sir Lionel. The castle was full of men at arms ready to defend themselves against the English soldiers. The only sound to be heard was the distant jingle of harness and the rumble of horses' hoofs!

The commander of the castle troops told Lancelot that the archers were ready to shoot their arrows from the castle walls. Every man was keyed-up ready.

Suddenly a knight on horseback left the ranks of Arthur's army and galloped towards the castle. Lancelot saw that it was King Arthur himself!

And so King Arthur, first of all the Knights of the Round Table, rode to the walls of Lancelot's castle and challenged the knight who had been his best friend to come and fight with him. A great hush came over the field. Will these two great knights really fight one another? *More next week.*

FRANK BELLAMY

King Arthur and his Knights

King Arthur has taken an army across the sea to France and reached the castle of the banished Lancelot. Arthur challenges Lancelot to fight him.

> Sir Lancelot, you are a false knight! Come out and fight with me!

King Arthur's voice rang up the great castle wall and echoed back over the plain, where his knights and soldiers were gathered for the great battle.

> Sir Lancelot, you must go and fight King Arthur.

> Never! Never! Never!

As Arthur's challenge rang out once more, Sir Lionel, who had thrown in his lot with the banished Lancelot, urged him strongly to fight the King.

> King Arthur has insulted you, Lancelot! You must fight him!

> No! I will fight any man on earth – but not King Arthur!

The faithful Sir Lionel was very upset that King Arthur had called Lancelot a false knight. But Lancelot was determined not to fight the King.

> You have wronged me, King Arthur, but I will not fight with you!

From the battlements Lancelot called to Arthur in a loud, mournful voice. He was sad that the King thought him false, but still he refused to fight!

> He is afraid to fight you, Sire! May I fight Lancelot?

> Any one of my knights may challenge him.

Then Gawaine, who was in league with the wicked Mordred, the knight responsible for Lancelot's banishment, asked permission to fight Lancelot.

Gawaine called out in a mocking voice and accused Lancelot of cowardice. Lancelot replied with fire and anger and accepted Gawaine's challenge.

When Lancelot accepted the challenge the boastful Gawaine asked King Arthur to ride away from the place of battle. The King rode away in silence.

The drawbridge of the castle fell with a great roar. Then, from the castle, in a terrific burst of speed, came the fearful figure of the angry Lancelot!

As Lancelot thundered over the plain, Sir Lionel watched from the battlements in great excitement. He even felt sorry for the boastful Gawaine!

The angry Lancelot swept down on Gawaine with great fury. His strong arm thrust the lance forward and struck Gawaine a mighty blow on the breastplate. The crafty knight was knocked aside and fell backwards from his saddle. Arthur's knights gasped as Sir Gawaine fell. *More next week.*

Ring Arthur and his Rnights

King Arthur has gone to France and challenged Lancelot to battle. Lancelot refuses Arthur's challenge but fights with the crafty Gawaine.

Sir Gawaine, a friend of the knight responsible for Lancelot's banishment, was knocked off his horse by one strong blow from the true and noble Lancelot.

King Arthur and his Knights saw Gawaine struck from his horse while Sir Lancelot rode by unscathed. The knights were forced to cry out in admiration of the strength and skill of the banished Lancelot. Then, one of the knights declared that he would issue yet another challenge to the great warrior!

Sir Lancelot reined in his horse and turned to face Arthur's army. Another knight had left the ranks and was galloping forward to challenge him!

The knight swept up to Lancelot and issued his challenge. Lancelot accepted at once. He was feeling strong, determined and certain of victory.

The earth trembled again beneath the pounding hoofs of the swift and splendid horses. The angry Lancelot thrust once more with his lance and again he scored a great blow. But as the knight reeled back in his saddle and fell to the ground, Lancelot's lance broke in two with the force of the mighty blow!

King Arthur cried out in admiration as he saw Lancelot's courage and skill. And yet another knight declared he would fight the brave Sir Lancelot!

The next knight then spurred his horse forward and shouted to King Arthur that the third fight would surely be the end of the valiant Lancelot!

From the battlements of the castle, Lancelot's comrades watched the scene below. Their hearts beat faster as a third knight rode out to challenge Lancelot, who had thrown away his broken lance and drawn his sword. Can Lancelot defend himself against this fully armed knight? *More next week.*

King Arthur and his Knights

Sir Lancelot has refused to fight King Arthur, but has just defeated two of his knights. Now a *third* knight is challenging the gallant Lancelot!

Lancelot awaited the attack of the galloping knight. His lance was broken and he had only his sword for defence but he sat firmly on his horse without fear.

The knight thrust fiercely with his lance, but Lancelot was too quick for him and ducked in his saddle. The lance just caught Lancelot's shoulder and flew out of the knight's hand. At the same time Lancelot swung with his sword and struck his opponent a terrific blow, which sent him reeling!

The knight rode past Sir Lancelot, then fell from his horse with a clatter of armour. Lancelot was tired after his fights but he stayed in the field.

And then a *fourth* knight was about to ride against Lancelot! But the King stopped him out of respect for the gallant Sir Lancelot's great feat of arms.

By the King's command there were no more challengers from the Knights of the Round Table. Very tired, but triumphant, the gallant Lancelot rode slowly back to his castle, cheered by both his friends and his enemies. It was a proud moment for this noble knight who had been treated so unfairly.

Of the three knights who had fought with Lancelot only the crafty Gawaine escaped serious hurt. He limped back to the army with a scowl on his face.

It was nearing the end of a long and weary day and King Arthur decided that his knights and soldiers should get some rest before the attack on the castle.

King Arthur's camp fires burned brightly while his army rested before the battle which would begin at dawn. The King's thoughts were still of Lancelot, whom he believed to be a traitor! Will Arthur ever find out that Lancelot is a true friend who has been the victim of a foul plot? *More next week.*

Lancelot has defeated three of Arthur's knights. King Arthur is about to attack Lancelot's castle with his great army of knights and soldiers.

In the grey morning light King Arthur gave his final orders. A terrific bombardment of Sir Lancelot's well-defended castle was now about to commence!

From the castle battlements Sir Lionel could see the full strength of Arthur's army. He felt worried, but the brave Lancelot was full of confidence.

As King Arthur made his plans on the plain below, Sir Lancelot prepared to defend his castle against the mighty English army which had invaded his lands.

King Arthur's attack began! The mighty catapults released huge stones which flew through the air and crashed against the French castle. At the same time

a long line of archers ran towards the castle walls, and the still morning air was shattered by the loud cries of Arthur's soldiers as they surged forward.

The great stones from Arthur's catapults made little impression on the castle walls. Lancelot's archers stood their ground and let fly a shower of arrows at the advancing soldiers and bowmen of King Arthur's army. The men scattered before the arrows which fell on to them like a rainstorm.

King Arthur was some distance from the castle walls but he longed to be in the thick of the battle. He rode forward, recklessly. His Captain shouted a warning.

The King rode through the ranks of his soldiers and archers. Arrows rained down from the castle walls, and Arthur's archers kept up their fire.

From the castle battlements, two of Lancelot's bowmen spied the galloping Arthur. In a flash, one of them raised his bow and shot an arrow at the King.

The arrow missed the King, but grazed his horse which reared up and threw Arthur from the saddle. He was at the mercy of the archers! *More next week.*

King Arthur and his Knights

King Arthur is besieging Sir Lancelot's castle in France. His horse is struck by an arrow and rears with fright, throwing King Arthur to the ground.

The King's horse threw him to the ground and galloped away. As King Arthur scrambled to his feet he made an easy target for Sir Lancelot's archers.

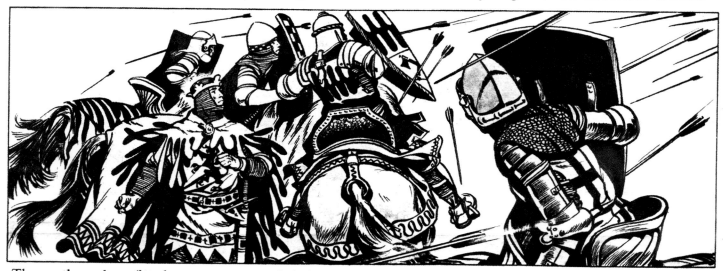

The castle archers fitted new arrows to their bows in great haste. Each one longed to shoot the English King who stood helpless on the plain. But a band of

Arthur's loyal knights galloped in front of the King and took the rain of arrows upon themselves! But he was still quite helpless without a mount.

King Arthur was not long without a horse, however. One of his knights rode up with another mount and the King ran forward to jump into the saddle.

Back in the saddle, the King shouted out his orders. He called for a greater bombardment of the castle walls and for more archers to be brought to the front.

But, later that day, after many huge stones had been hurled at Lancelot's castle and after many raids by the English archers, the army of King Arthur was forced to retreat. The strong walls of the castle had withstood the bombardment and Lancelot's archers were still shooting their arrows with deadly skill.

The gallant Lancelot watched the retreat with the good knight Lionel. The fierce fighting had come to an end. Soon the night would close in about them.

The brave Sir Lancelot turned from the battlements to go to his room and take a well-earned rest. He gave his last orders for the day to his Commander.

King Arthur sat with his knights and discussed the fighting. All were agreed that Lancelot's castle was a great fortress that would not yield easily. And then the King's thoughts strayed to his own castle in England. What was happening at Camelot, and what was Mordred doing? *More next week.*

61

King Arthur and his Knights

King Arthur is fighting in France. In England, the false knight, Mordred, who has been left in charge of the kingdom, is planning to seize the throne.

King Arthur and his Knights are busy in France! Only Sir Kay, Merlin and one or two others to get rid of! Soon, I will be King of England!

At Camelot, Sir Mordred was gloating over the success of his plot. He felt sure that with Arthur out of the way, he would soon be King in place of him.

Sir Mordred, a troop of knights is approaching the castle!

At last! Here are the men who are going to serve me.

A messenger rushed into the room and told Mordred that a band of men was nearing the castle. These were Mordred's supporters – ready to betray King Arthur.

Merlin! Strange knights are approaching!

Let us go to the battlements.

In the court-yard, Merlin, King Arthur's counsellor, was greeted by the King's steward, Sir Kay, with the news of the men who were riding to Camelot.

I don't like the look of these knights, Merlin!

They all look villains! Friends of Mordred, no doubt!

On the battlements Sir Kay and Merlin watched the troop of knights ride to the castle gate. By this time both Kay and Merlin had become suspicious of

Sir Mordred and they were alarmed to see such a strong force of evil-looking men riding into Camelot. For what purpose had they come to the castle?

The troop of knights clattered over the drawbridge into the castle court-yard. They were greeted by Sir Mordred who was full of glee. Now he had a band of armed men who would obey his orders! In the background Merlin and Sir Kay watched the scene. Now they realised that Mordred was a traitor.

Sir Kay asked Mordred why these strange knights had come to the King's castle. Mordred was very angry that his power should be questioned by Sir Kay.

In a great rage, Mordred left Kay and Merlin. He knew they were suspicious of his motives, and he decided to take action against them without delay.

Kay and Merlin were now convinced of Mordred's evil designs. Merlin urged Kay to get to France at all costs and to warn Arthur of the dangers at home in England. In great haste the young Sir Kay strapped on his sword and prepared to make a dash from the castle. Will Kay get right away? *More next week.*

Ring Arthur and his Rnights

While King Arthur is fighting Lancelot in France, Merlin and Kay have realised that Sir Mordred is a traitor. Kay is about to leave Camelot for France.

The King's steward Sir Kay, exchanged goodbyes with old Merlin and made for the door. He was in a great hurry to get to France.

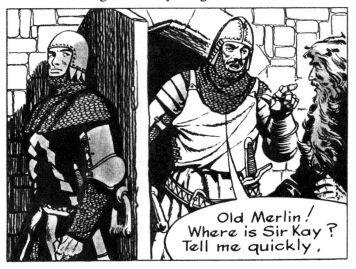

Sir Kay had his hand on the door when he heard the tramp of footsteps in the passage. Merlin urged Kay to hide behind the door.

Sir Kay stepped aside as the door burst open. One of Mordred's villainous knights stood there and he called to Merlin in a loud and coarse voice.

As the knight stepped into the room, Sir Kay came out from behind the door. In a flash the knight's sword whistled through the air, grazing Sir Kay's

head, and bit deep into the open door. Merlin threw up his arms with excitement and Sir Kay skilfully dodged out of the door.

Sir Kay flew down a steep flight of steps which led to the stables where his valiant horse was waiting. There wasn't a moment to lose!

Sir Kay sprang on to his horse and galloped furiously across the castle courtyard. The gate was still open and the drawbridge was down.

Stop him! Bring him down!

Sir Kay thundered through the castle gate. Behind him Sir Mordred came running and shouting. A man hurled a spear at Kay, but his aim was wild.

The King's steward flew from the castle like a bird in his great bid to reach France with the news of Mordred's treacherous plans.

After him! Bring him back dead or alive!

Two of Mordred's knights pursued Sir Kay out of the castle. Mordred was furious that the King's steward had escaped from his clutches so easily.

I do not care if Kay escapes to France. In a few days time I shall make myself King of England. Arthur is finished!

In spite of Sir Kay's escape Mordred was confident that he would make himself King. Will Arthur return in time to save his throne? *More next week.*

King Arthur and his Knights

While Arthur fights in France, Mordred plans to seize power in England. The King's steward, Sir Kay, is escaping to France with the news.

Two of Mordred's knights came into the courtyard with the wise old Merlin who was now a prisoner. Mordred told them to shut up Merlin in a cell.

As the two men dragged him away, the wise old Merlin, who was quite without fear, warned Mordred that King Arthur would return and be revenged!

Mordred's plans were completed when one of the rebel knights told him that all Arthur's friends had been imprisoned. Mordred was master of Camelot!

And then Mordred went into the great hall of the castle and stood before the Round Table where King Arthur had sat so often at the head of his

Knights. And Mordred cried out in a loud boastful voice that the noble Arthur, whom he had betrayed, was now King no more!

I have shaken them off. I shall be in Cardiff by nightfall.

Meanwhile, Sir Kay had eluded Mordred's knights who had pursued him from Camelot. He hoped to reach the port of Cardiff before it was dark.

I must find a ship to take me to France immediately.

Sir Kay reached Cardiff safely. He had a meal at an inn and then hurried to the harbour. He just had to reach France as soon as possible!

Here is gold. I must sail for France tonight!

Tonight it is, sir!

At the harbour, Sir Kay found an old sea captain and offered him a bag of gold if he would agree to set sail instantly for France.

Some time later an English ship sailed into a small French port. Sir Kay was on board. He had made the difficult crossing in record time.

Goodbye, Captain!

As soon as the ship dropped anchor Sir Kay rushed ashore with his horse. He jumped into the saddle, waved goodbye to the captain and galloped away.

Like an arrow from a bow, the quick Sir Kay sped across the fields of France. Is King Arthur still besieging Lancelot's castle? And will Kay find him?
More next week.

King Arthur and his Knights

Mordred has seized power in England while Arthur is fighting Lancelot in France. Sir Kay, the King's steward, escapes to France in search of Arthur.

In his camp before Lancelot's castle, King Arthur listened gravely to his Captain. Many knights had fallen sick and still Lancelot held his fortress.

While Arthur was listening to the Captain's report a servant rushed up to the King and announced the arrival of an unknown knight on horseback.

Sir Kay had triumphed in his great bid to reach King Arthur in France. He rode into the camp and was directed immediately to the King's side.

And so the valiant Sir Kay, the King's steward, reached the end of his journey. He reined in his tired horse before the astonished Arthur, who thought his steward at home in Camelot. Gawaine, who worked for Mordred, was surprised to see one of Arthur's Knights arrive from England!

The weary Sir Kay called out in a loud voice for all to hear that Sir Mordred was a traitor who had broken his oath to his King and betrayed him!

The crafty Gawaine protested that Sir Kay was not telling the truth. But Arthur silenced Gawaine. He knew that his steward was a most honest knight.

Sir Kay called out once more and begged Arthur to take his knights and soldiers back across the sea to England. King Arthur, deeply shocked by the awful news of Mordred's treachery, shouted a command to his knights and captains that they should now abandon the siege of Lancelot's castle!

From the battlements of his besieged castle the brave Sir Lancelot looked on in amazement as King Arthur with his knights and soldiers abandoned their camp and began their retreat to the coast. Will King Arthur reach England in time to save his throne from Mordred? And what will Lancelot do now?

King Arthur and his Knights

Sir Kay has fled to France to tell King Arthur that Mordred is a traitor and a false knight. Arthur has abandoned his siege of Lancelot's castle.

> Gallop to the sea! Tell the captains to make our ships ready! We must sail at once for England!

As the King's army retreated to the sea, Arthur gave orders that his fleet of ships should be made ready immediately to take his soldiers on board.

> Gawaine, keep watch at our rear! Sir Kay, you ride with me at the head of the army!

King Arthur sent the baffled Gawaine to the rear of the army, while his brave steward, Sir Kay, rode by his side at the head of all the knights.

> King Arthur is too late! Sir Mordred will take the throne of England!

The false knight, Gawaine, no longer enjoyed Arthur's favours, but he felt sure that the wicked Mordred would seize the throne from the King!

> Are my ships ready for sea?

> Yes, your Majesty! We sail at sunset. You will soon see England again!

Arthur's army moved at great speed and soon reached the coast of France, where the great fleet of ships was waiting. The commander of the ships was on the shore to meet the King, and reported that all was ready for the voyage back to England where Arthur would have to fight for his throne!

And so, by sunset, Arthur's great force had boarded the ships which sped without delay from France, towards the open sea and England!

Goodbye France! Goodbye Lancelot! What terrible wrong have I done to this most noble knight?

Standing in the stern of his swift ship, King Arthur thought with sadness of his expedition in France. Was Sir Lancelot really his true friend after all?

Boy! Find my steward, Sir Kay and send him to my cabin.

At once, Sire!

The unhappy King paced the reeling deck of his ship. Then he called to his page and asked for his steward, the brave and faithful Sir Kay.

Sir Kay, I am sick at heart. Tell me what has happened in England while I have been away.

Sir Kay went to Arthur's cabin. The King was sad and troubled and asked his steward to tell the sorry story of the great plot against his throne.

.... Mordred has filled Camelot with false knights. He has won power throughout the land. You must now fight against your own countrymen!

Alas, I have been a foolish King! I have trusted the false knight Mordred, and wronged the true knight Lancelot!

King Arthur and Sir Kay talked deep into the night as the ship surged across the dark sea. Sir Kay told the King of Mordred's treachery, and Arthur was stirred with anger and regret as he heard the bitter tale. Very soon he must fight for his life, his honour, and his throne!   *More next week.*

King Arthur and his Knights

King Arthur has been besieging Lancelot's castle in France. Now he is returning to England to fight the wicked Mordred and his rebel army.

The beaches are deserted your Majesty. All the boats are ready for landing.

As King Arthur's fine fleet drew near the shores of England, the commander of the ships reported that all was ready for the landing of men and supplies.

Mordred is bound to be close at hand. I will lead the men on shore myself!

From the deck of his ship, Arthur and Sir Kay scanned the deserted shore. The King knew that Mordred and his army must be close at hand.

Be careful of your life, Sire!

I am to blame, Sir Kay, that we must now fight our own people. My life is not important.

King Arthur felt himself to blame for the war he would have to wage against his own countrymen, and ignored Kay's warning not to take any risks.

A short while later the army of knights and soldiers waded through the shallows of Dover Beach. King Arthur had returned from his expedition with few losses, but as his feet sank once more into the English sands he knew that much bitter fighting must be done before he could call himself King again.

When King Arthur's army was half-way up the beach, a long line of archers stood up from their hiding places at the top of the hill. At a word of command from the false Mordred the deadly arrows hummed through the air like a cloud of angry bees to wound the weary soldiers as they stumbled on.

King Arthur stood firm in the centre of the ranks as his men halted before the fierce and stinging arrows and called on them to follow him.

Arthur burst forward with a group of his knights and broke the line of archers who were still firing their deadly arrows down on to the unsheltered beach.

The rest of the soldiers swarmed up the beach. Arthur was in great fighting mood and called out on the traitor Mordred, who had betrayed his trust.

And then Arthur came face to face with Mordred, and called with an angry voice upon the traitor who had wrecked his Kingdom! *More next week*.

King Arthur and his Knights

King Arthur's knights and soldiers have landed at Dover to fight wicked Mordred. After fierce fighting on the beach Arthur comes face to face with him.

Arthur and Mordred met with a terrific clash of swords. They stood for a moment with weapons locked. Arthur was angry and Mordred full of hatred.

Suddenly, one of Mordred's rebel soldiers crept up behind the King, and with a great cry of triumph swung a heavy club against the side of Arthur's head.

As King Arthur crashed to the ground the false knight Mordred raised his sword and prepared to plunge it into the body of the defenceless King!

Out of the battle came the King's steward, Sir Kay, together with a loyal knight. They challenged Mordred with ringing voices as the false knight

threatened the life of the fallen King. Mordred's hand faltered and he quailed with fear as the two fearsome knights rushed upon him with swords drawn.

And then Sir Mordred turned tail and ran for his life. Sir Kay hurled his sword like a lance and it whistled past Sir Mordred's ear as he vanished into the battle. The other knight went on his knees to be with the King who lay as still as a log, with no sign of life at all. He gently tended him.

The unconscious body of King Arthur was placed on a stretcher and, escorted by knights, was quickly borne away to a sheltered corner of the field.

Although swordless, Sir Kay pursued the cowardly Mordred. But the false knight had ordered his soldiers to retreat. Sir Kay rushed back to the King.

When Kay reached the King he found a surgeon tending Arthur's wounds. He was relieved to hear that he was not badly hurt and would get well.

The King recovered and declared that Mordred and his traitors would soon fight their last battle. Will Arthur rule in peace again? *More next week.*

King Arthur and his Knights

King Arthur has returned from France and has fought a battle with the traitor Mordred at Dover. Mordred runs away. King Arthur is wounded.

In spite of his wounds King Arthur was full of fight. He could find no rest until Mordred's power in the land had been overthrown.

The Commander of the army reported heavy casualties to the King. When Arthur learned that false Gawaine was badly hurt, he asked to see him.

Sir Gawaine, Mordred's friend, was dying. He begged Arthur to forgive him, and spoke in glowing words of the true and brave Lancelot.

King Arthur was moved by Gawaine's confession, and he cried out for forgiveness himself from the knight he had so cruelly wronged.

Arthur turned away from the wretched Gawaine and walked back to the head of his army. He gave orders to pursue Mordred as soon as possible.

Meanwhile, in France, a messenger burst into the castle hall where Lancelot was sitting with Sir Lionel. When Lancelot heard the news of Arthur's desperate battle with Mordred, he sprang from his chair and with a generous impulse declared that he would sail for England and fight for Arthur's cause!

As Lancelot rushed along the castle corridor, Lionel reminded him of Arthur's unjust treatment, but Lancelot loved his King and would die for him!

A few hours later, Sir Lancelot swept from his castle with a party of specially chosen knights. They rode at speed to the coast of France.

The careful sea captain was fearful of his ship's chances in the rough sea, but Sir Lancelot would not wait, and demanded to sail without delay.

Lancelot and the captain stood in the forepeak as the ship headed out into the sea. Great waves broke over the deck. Will Lancelot reach England?
More next week.

Ring Arthur and his Rnights

Although Arthur has treated Lancelot badly, the brave knight is sailing after the King to help him fight wicked Mordred. But Lancelot's ship is delayed.

Meanwhile, in England, Arthur had recovered from his wound. A young knight, Sir Bedivere, told him that Mordred had formed an army on Salisbury Plain.

The people who lived in the small towns and villages ran from their houses to see King Arthur with his knights and soldiers pressing along the same road that Mordred had taken a few days ago. The people were puzzled by the warlike men who were roaming over the country. They all longed for peace.

Arthur and Sir Kay rode at the head of the army over the Plain. Then suddenly, a horseman appeared on the horizon. He was galloping like the wind!

The messenger reined in his horse before the King. He came from Mordred, and brought the surprising news that the wicked knight wanted peace in the land!

Tell Mordred we will talk with him tomorrow, as soon as it is light!

In the morning our fate will be decided. If Mordred surrenders, all is well. If not, we must fight him to the death!

King Arthur found it hard to believe that the shifty Mordred truly desired to be at peace with him, but he agreed to meet and talk with him the next day.

That night, the King could not sleep at all. He sat up in his tent listening to the wind whistling over the Plain, and the thoughts raced round in his head.

Sire, it is daybreak and time to ride to the battlefield.

I am ready, Sir Kay.

Sir Mordred, King Arthur and his Knights are already in the field!

We will go to meet them!

At the crack of dawn, Arthur's faithful steward, Sir Kay, came to his tent to rouse him, but the King was already dressed in his full and splendid armour.

A short while later, Sir Mordred had the news that Arthur was already in the field. The meeting of the King and the traitor knight was at hand!

King Arthur! All I want is peace!

Mordred, you lie! All you want is war!

When the mists had vanished from the great Plain, two armies were revealed, facing one another, standing quite still just like trees on either side of a

long straight road. Arthur did not believe Mordred, who had brought such ruin to the land. Will the two armies fight to the end?   *More next week.*

King Arthur and his Knights

On the great Plain near Salisbury, King Arthur and his knights have met the rebel army of the false knight Mordred who says he wants peace in the land.

Although King Arthur could never trust Mordred again, he agreed to talk with the knight in the hope of saving the misery and bloodshed of a great battle.

King Arthur had a last word with his steward, Sir Kay, and warned him to be on the look-out lest Mordred's army should launch a sudden attack.

Then Arthur, true King of Britain, rode to meet Sir Mordred, that wicked knight who had destroyed the King's friendship with the brave Lancelot.

Once more Sir Mordred protested that he desired peace above all things. And the two men talked earnestly while both the armies watched in silence.

And then, while King Arthur talked with Mordred, a poisonous snake slid out of the tall heather and struck at the foot of one of Mordred's soldiers.

The soldier of Mordred's army looked down and saw the snake writhing about his feet. With a sudden cry of fear he drew his sword and struck at the snake. As he did so, a great shout of alarm came from the distant Sir Kay who had seen the bright blade flashing in the air, and at once suspected treachery!

Both King Arthur and Sir Mordred were surprised by Sir Kay's shout of alarm, but before they knew what was happening the trumpets of war had sounded and the air was filled with cries. Then they accused one another of treachery, but neither of them knew the cause of the upset.

The battle broke in all its fury. King Arthur's knights swept to the attack to be met by a great force of Mordred's knights. In the bitter clash that followed, many knights were tumbled from their horses by the thrusting lances. Now the fateful battle had begun! Where is Lancelot? *More next week.*

King Arthur and his Knights

Arthur and Mordred are fighting a last desperate battle on Salisbury Plain. Sir Lancelot is sailing from France to help the King who has treated him unjustly.

After weathering heavy storms at sea, Lancelot's ship sighted England. He was most upset that the storms had delayed him in his bid to help Arthur.

Sir Lionel, get the horses ashore – quickly!

As the ship came close to the sea wall, Sir Lancelot jumped impatiently ashore. He called to Sir Lionel to get the knights and horses on land as soon as possible.

Where are the armies of King Arthur and the traitor Mordred?

Sir, they are fighting on Salisbury Plain!

Sir Lancelot immediately seized the harbour master and demanded to know urgently the whereabouts of King Arthur and the false knight Mordred.

We must ride like the wind! There is no time to lose!

Very soon all Lancelot's knights were ashore and mounted on their horses. They swept through the main streets of the port, urged on by the gallant and bold Sir Lancelot, whose one aim was to reach the battlefield, and there to fight at King Arthur's side in the battle which would decide the fate of the Kingdom.

As darkness fell over Salisbury Plain, the battle between the two armies was still raging. Arthur, who had fought like a tiger all day, came together with his knights, Lucan and Bedivere. To Arthur's great sorrow he learnt that his steward, the sweet-natured Sir Kay, had died during the fighting that day.

King Arthur cried out in grief over the death of Sir Kay, most faithful of all knights, and spoke ill of Mordred who had fought in the rear of his army.

The weary and battle-stained King said they would fight again on the morrow to try for victory in this most bitter struggle against the treacherous Mordred.

Early the next morning, the battle began again. The King rode out with a small band. In the distance they spied Mordred and his troop of knights.

Arthur's blood was up. With a cry he spurred his horse forward to charge upon the traitor knight and to fight him to the death. *More next week.*

King Arthur and his Knights

It is the second day of the great battle with Mordred's rebel army. King Arthur is charging Mordred's troop with his band of knights.

As King Arthur and his knights galloped over Salisbury Plain, Sir Mordred realised that he must stand and fight for his life against the angry King.

The rival knights clashed with great force. King Arthur had drawn his mighty sword Excalibur and, cutting about him, he burst through the ring of knights in search of Sir Mordred. With one great blow he unseated one of Sir Mordred's finest men. No one could stop the fierce and noble young King!

And so the King came face to face with Sir Mordred for the last time. The heavily armoured horses reared with excitement as the two men greeted one another with war-like cries. Then King Arthur lifted Excalibur above his head while Sir Mordred lowered his powerful lance to thrust it at the King!

The two warriors clashed with all the force they could muster. Each was set on victory and they plied their arms with great skill. Arthur caught Mordred a fearful blow with Excalibur, while Mordred's lance went surely home. The two knights reeled in their saddles and fell heavily to the ground.

Sir Bedivere and Sir Lucan, both victorious, were just in time to see King Arthur fall, badly wounded, from his horse. They rode to his aid at top speed.

Sir Bedivere leapt from his horse and ran to the fallen King. In a faint voice, he told the knight to carry him away. He said his wounds were fatal.

They carried him near to a great sheet of water far from the cry of battle and there laid him on the bank. Sir Bedivere had brought the sword Excalibur.

King Arthur was dying. As he lay on the bank, faint from his mortal wounds, he learnt that Sir Mordred was dead and the battle won. *More next week.*

King Arthur and his Knights

King Arthur has killed the treacherous knight Sir Mordred in a great battle and regained his kingdom. But the King has been mortally wounded.

Sir Bedivere, I am dying. If you see Lancelot again, beg him to forgive me for all the wrong I have done him.

I will, Sire.

The dying King's thoughts were still of Lancelot who had been his best friend and the most noble of knights. Arthur longed for Lancelot to forgive him.

Take my sword Excalibur, and throw it out there —into the water.

And then King Arthur told Sir Bedivere to take up the mighty sword, Excalibur, and to throw it straight and true into the middle of the vast sheet of water.

But Sire, this sword is wonderful and precious.....

Do as I say!

Sir Bedivere was astonished at this command and began to argue with the King. But again Arthur told the knight to throw the sword into the water.

The reluctant Sir Bedivere made a powerful throw. The precious sword left his hand and skimmed through the air like a sharp silver bird of prey.

As the great and trusty sword was about to plunge into the water, a strong hand came up from the deep and caught the sword cleanly by the hilt!

The hand brandished the sword three times, then drew it gently beneath the surface of the water. Sir Bedivere gasped at this incredible sight. King Arthur remembered the day when he first received Excalibur from the lake near Camelot. He knew then that his hour had come. And so King Arthur died.

Sir Bedivere was full of grief and wept long over the body of the dead King. He could not believe that the great King Arthur was now no more.

As Sir Bedivere mourned, knights left their horses and formed a quiet circle round the dead King. The air was still and the water like glass.

As the knights stood in silence before the body of their King, the Plain shook with the thunder of galloping horses. At first the knights did not know the band of men. Then they saw the challenging form of Sir Lancelot and they marvelled, believing him to be in France. He had come too late!
More next week.

King Arthur and his Knights

King Arthur is dead. After a great fight he killed the false knight Mordred, then died himself when his mighty sword, Excalibur was thrown into the water.

Here comes Sir Lancelot!

Sir Bedivere stood with his fellow knights by the dead King. And then the brave Sir Lancelot who had just arrived from France, galloped up with his men.

Sir Lancelot, if you came to kill the King, you are too late. Arthur is dead.

I came to save his life! To fight by his side! To help him win back his throne from the traitor Mordred!

Sir Lancelot and his men reined in their tired horses before the silent group of knights. Sir Bedivere thought that Lancelot might have rushed to England to take his revenge on Arthur, but the true and noble knight had come to save the King from his enemies and he deeply mourned that he had arrived too late.

Mordred was slain by King Arthur, and his army has been vanquished!

We must take the King to his castle at Camelot.

Sir Lancelot and his knights listened intently to Sir Bedivere's tale of the woeful death of King Arthur after the great fight with Sir Mordred.

Is the castle still held by Mordred's men?

Yes, Lancelot, but our army is advancing there now. The castle will soon surrender.

King Arthur's body was borne away to a carriage. Sir Bedivere assured Sir Lancelot that Camelot would soon be in the hands of the King's army.

Some time later, the funeral of King Arthur passed through the castle gates. The fields on either side, and the battlements above, were crowded with loyal soldiers. The vast throng was silent; the only sounds were the jingle of harness and the horses' muffled hooves. The King was back in his castle.

Inside the courtyard, the King's old counsellor, Merlin, who had been released from his dungeon, ran forward to greet Sir Lancelot with tears of joy!

Old Merlin spoke with great feeling and begged Sir Lancelot to assemble the Knights of the Round Table so that the country might be united again.

In the hall of Camelot Castle, King Arthur's Knights gathered once more before the Round Table. Lancelot stood on one side of the vacant chair, and Merlin on the other. And so, in a most solemn scene, these knights swore to keep peace in the country, as the great reign of King Arthur came to an end.

The Swiss Family Robinson

Originally published in Zurich in two volumes in 1812-13 as *Der schweizerische Robinson; oder, Der schiffbrüchige Schweizerprediger und seine Familie*, the book we know today as *Swiss Family Robinson* is something of a hotchpotch of the original text and material freely added at various times by other writers, editors and translators. The story was originally told in instalments by pastor Johann David Wyss for the entertainment of his four sons. Wyss (1743-1818), a Swiss army chaplain born in Bern, had read them Defoe's *Robinson Crusoe* and followed it with his own version of shipwreck and survival on an uninhabited island.

Its debt to *Robinson Crusoe* goes far beyond the title: Wyss carried many incidents from Defoe's narrative into his storyline – searching a ship-wreck, building various houses, planting crops, animal husbandry – but his intentions were to educate as well as entertain. Much of the narrative is instructional and the father in the story – like Wyss a pastor with four sons – uses their various adventures to explain the principals of natural history and physical sciences. Even as they escape the trapped vessel in the opening chapter, the narrator pauses to explain the principals of Archimedes' lever to his eldest son. Not surprisingly, the book is filled with Christian virtue and morals.

Wyss had put the story in writing but the manuscript sat for many years, disorganised and incomplete, until his son, Johann Rudolf Wyss (1782-1830), by then a Professor of Philosophy at the academy at Bern, edited the story for publication. In the original publication, the story comes to a somewhat unsatisfactory ending: after two years on the island, the narrator wonders whether his family will ever see another human face again. A postscript by the editor notes that, a few years later, a ship discovers the island and the narrator's journal is passed to the Captain.

The story soon found its way into France in a translation by Mme. Isabelle de Montolieu, a Swiss novelist and translator, as *Le Robinson suisse, ou, Journal d'un père de famille, naufragé avec ses enfans* (1814); by arrangement with Wyss, Montolieu expanded the story and it was this version which was first translated into English by William Godwin and published in 1814 under the title *The Family Robinson Crusoe*. Mme. de Montolieu further expanded the story in 1824-26, adding many exciting incidents for the children and it is this expanded version that was translated – and abridged considerably – by W. H. G. Kingston in 1889, which has been the basis for most subsequent editions, which themselves were abridged and rewritten to suit whatever audience the publisher was aiming at.

The *Swift* version of the story, under the more common *Swiss Family Robinson* title first used in 1818, follows a later translation of the story in which the youngest son has become known as Francis (rather than Franz) and Jack has become James; episodes such as the appearance of a python in episode 26 and the arrival of Jenny, a young English girl shipwrecked on a nearby rock, are amongst the scenes added by later writers.

Bellamy's artwork is exemplary throughout, although with ten frames to the page his work is a little cramped. He does a wonderful job of illustrating the island's incredible range of wildlife – everything from kangaroos and penguins to buffalo and budgerigars – yet the strip suffers from the simplicity of storytelling, being little more than a catalogue of weekly discoveries. The threats to the family's harmony seem mild and are easily overcome, clearing the way for next week's survival or nature lesson.

As the strip was the first that Bellamy drew from start to finish, *Swiss Family Robinson* has some historical interest but, truth be told, the interest is not much more than as a stepping stone towards the far superior *King Arthur*.

The Robinson family left Switzerland to find a new country. Just as land was sighted their ship struck a rock.

The sailors took the only boats, and left the Robinsons behind.

Mr Robinson said they would try to get ashore in the morning.

They made a boat. James wanted to take the ship's dogs with them.

They piled the boat up. It creaked and groaned under the weight. The cow had to wait for the next trip!

Fritz found a good spot to land, near the mouth of a small river. They discovered they were on an island.

They made a tent from a sail. Poor James found a lobster!

Supper was eaten by the light of the fire. They used shells for spoons.

Soon they were asleep. The fire would frighten any wild animals away.

The Robinson family have left their home in Switzerland to find a new land. They are ship-wrecked on a desert island. There is plenty of food on the island.

Mr Robinson wanted to find out if there were any other people on the island. Fritz and the two dogs went with him.

It seems to be coming this way.

Don't shoot till you can see it properly.

It looks as though we are the only people on the island.

When something moved in the bushes, Fritz raised his gun.

But it was only their two dogs, Turk and Belle.

Mr Robinson and Fritz searched the island. There was no sign of anyone from the wreck.

The juice in this stick tastes sweet.

They must be sugar canes.

At the camp.

A monkey showered them with coconuts, which they kept.

They found some sugar cane to take back to the camp.

Ernest shot a goose, and James and Francis caught some fish.

May I carry him, Fritz?

What is the bundle of sticks for?

Tomorrow we must go to the ship to fetch the rest of the animals.

That night.

More next week

Fritz found a baby mongoose. It would protect them from the snakes.

What a wonderful supper they had of roast goose.

Jackals came prowling round the tent, but the guns scared them off.

The Robinsons left their home in Switzerland to find a new land. They were ship-wrecked on a desert island. Mrs Robinson said she would like a tree-house built.

The Robinsons, with the animals they rescued from the ship, travelled to where they were going to build the house.

The dogs had a fight with a fierce porcupine. James shot it.

The donkey bolted when he felt the porcupine's quills.

The tree they wanted to build the house in looked much too high.

But Mr Robinson shot a rope tied to an arrow over a bough.

Then they fixed up a rope-ladder and started building.

They had to camp on the ground till the house was ready.

The house began to take shape. They used a ship's sail for the roof.

Fritz shot a wildcat he saw prowling near.

The tree-house was finished at last. They felt safe that night.

THE SWISS FAMILY ROBINSON

The Robinsons left their home in Switzerland to find a new land, and were ship-wrecked on an island. They built a house in a great tree and called it Falcons' Nest.

We shall never go short of food while we have potatoes growing.

Look! Pineapples! They're much better than potatoes.

One Sunday morning the Robinsons went out for a walk and found there were pineapples and potatoes on the island.

Don't forget to bring me a barrel of butter.

Mr Robinson, Fritz and Ernest went to the tent for stores.

Help! He's pulling me in!

Hang on! I'll help you to land him.

Ernest caught a huge salmon. Fritz helped him to land it.

Don't shoot! It won't do us any harm.

The dogs disturbed a kangaroo. Fritz was going to shoot, but his father stopped him.

Fritz and I must go to the ship tomorrow to get some more clothes.

The children only had one set of clothes.

I know, but I'll take some and a watch each for Ernest and James.

Money and jewellery aren't much good to us here.

Mr Robinson and Fritz found many valuables on the wreck.

Fritz saw a very big turtle asleep on the sea and caught it. They needed it for food.

They landed the turtle and unloaded the stores and other useful things.

What are you going to do with the money, Francis?

Buy some sweets when I see a sweet-shop again!

Francis and James were thrilled with the watches and money.

Now we shall have proper beds to sleep on instead of hammocks.

More next week

They packed the stores under the roots of the great tree.

The Robinson family left their home in Switzerland to find a new land. They were ship-wrecked on a desert island, where they built a house in a great tree.

Mr Robinson was woken up by a storm. He was worried that the boats would be swept away by the sea.

Next morning Mr Robinson and Fritz hurried to the beach.

They were only just in time. The rope had frayed on a rock.

Mr Robinson fetched the donkey, who pulled as hard as he could.

The precious stores were saved and loaded carefully on to the sledge.

Then they went back to the tree-house.

Later James went with his father and Fritz to fetch all they could from the wreck.

Fritz saw something and called out to the others.

Mr Robinson and the boys forced the boards open.

What a discovery – a fine boat! But how were they to get it into the water?

95

The SWISS FAMILY ROBINSON

The Robinson family left their home in Switzerland to find a new land. They were ship-wrecked on a desert island and built a house in a great tree. There was plenty to eat on the island.

As Mr Robinson helped Fritz with the stores, he hoped they would be able to launch the boat they had found.

They took back a wheelbarrow James had found on the wreck.

You'll never be able to feed it!

James decided to catch a penguin for a pet, but Fritz did not like the idea.

The penguins could not run fast, and James caught two.

But James soon lost his two new pets. They leapt from his arms into the sea.

When the corn grows Mother will bake a cake for us.

Mrs Robinson had started to plant her own corn.

But we can't eat poisonous cakes!

Meanwhile, Mr Robinson fetched a poisonous plant for flour.

He showed them what to do and they chopped up the roots.

James is the best jumper!

This is fun!

Then James and Ernest squeezed out the poison by jumping on the roots.

You're eating them as fast as I can make them!

More next week

Mrs Robinson made some cassava cakes from the flour.

The Robinson family left their home in Switzerland to find a new land. They were ship-wrecked on an island. They found a fine boat on the wreck but could not get it off.

Fritz, James and Ernest loaded stores on their boat. Mr Robinson was busy with something elsewhere.

As their boat neared the beach Mr Robinson pulled harder.

They had just landed when there was a loud explosion.

The boys ran to see if anything had happened to the wreck.

James got wet on the way to the wreck.

Mr Robinson had planted explosive on the wreck to blow a hole in it.

Next morning they launched the boat through the hole in the wreck.

Then they all set to work and put the boat's sail up.

As they neared the island they fired a salute with the cannons.

More next week.

Then they named the boat the *Elizabeth*, after Mrs Robinson.

97

The *Robinson family* left their home in Switzerland to find a new land. They were ship-wrecked on an island. They saved a fine boat from the wreck and called it the *Elizabeth*.

The *Elizabeth* was safely tied up. The Robinson family returned to their tree-house feeling very happy.

Mr Robinson and Ernest went for a walk. Coconuts started falling!

James ran up and saw that a big crab was making the coconuts fall.

James threw a stick at the crab. The crab began to chase him.

But James was too clever for the crab. He trapped it neatly in his shirt.

Mrs Robinson didn't like the crab one bit. They decided to cook it.

Ernest and James went for water to cook the crab in.

But they rushed back and said that they had seen a wild boar.

Mr Robinson and the boys stood and watched for it to appear.

But it was the Robinsons' own tame pig! They felt very silly.

The Robinson Family left their home in Switzerland to find a new land. They were ship-wrecked on a desert island where they built a house in a great tree.

Mrs Robinson and Francis went for a walk. They saw a huge creature asleep. Francis thought it was a crocodile.

Ernest said it couldn't have been a crocodile.

Mr Robinson and Ernest went to look for the creature. They soon found it.

Mr Robinson whistled, woke the animal and slipped a loop over its head.

It was an iguana, a very large lizard – an ugly creature.

On the way home they saw lots of budgerigars. Fritz wanted one.

But when he reached up to try to catch one, it nipped his finger.

Fritz caught one of the budgerigars. He showed it to his mother.

But back at the tree-house the bird pecked Fritz's finger and escaped.

More next week.

That evening the family had a tasty lizard for supper.

99

The Robinson family left their home in Switzerland to find a new land. They were ship-wrecked on a desert island, where they built a house in a great tree.

While Fritz and Ernest went exploring, James and Mr Robinson started to build a small donkey cart.

Ernest picked some wax berries from nearby.

Mr Robinson and James finished the cart. James backed the donkey into the shafts.

Ernest and Fritz melted the wax berries and made some candles.

Mrs Robinson was worried. The boys' clothes were wearing out.

The family returned to the wreck to collect more stores.

They collected everything and looked round sadly.

Mr Robinson decided to blow up the wreck to use for timber.

The fuse was lit, and the family left quickly.

Mrs Robinson held her ears as the powder went off with a big bang.

Useful timber from the wreck was washed in by the tide. Mr Robinson and Fritz collected it together.

Mrs Robinson had thought of a way to make butter.

Fritz said that they should make a map of the island.

Names were given to places on the map. Falcon's Nest was the tree-house.

The Robinsons set out to explore the whole island. It was very exciting.

They stopped near Cape Disappointment. The boys asked for a drink.

Fritz and James climbed up the coconut trees.

Ernest climbed a tree. There were no coconuts on it.

But Ernest climbed to the top and found a palm cabbage.

As the Robinson family got ready to camp for the night, the donkey suddenly bolted.

THE SWISS FAMILY ROBINSON

The Robinson family left their home in Switzerland to find a new land. They were ship-wrecked on an island and built a house in a tree. They were very worried when the donkey ran away.

Mr Robinson was afraid the donkey had been scared by wild animals. He decided to keep watch all night.

Next day he and James searched for the donkey.

Suddenly Mr Robinson and James came face to face with some buffaloes!

James shot the fiercest buffalo, and all but a young one ran away.

They were going to take it back with them and put it with their other animals.

They put ropes on the buffalo and got it home, with the help of Belle.

Mrs Robinson fed the buffalo with potatoes.

Later the boys found a young eagle in a nest on the cliffs.

They decided to catch it and take it back home with them.

More next week.

Mr Robinson blew smoke on the young eagle to make it sleepy.

The Robinson family left their home in Switzerland to find a new land. They were ship-wrecked on an island, where they build a snug house in a great tree.

The Robinsons explored a new part of the island. On the way home they discovered that the pig had some babies.

Mr Robinson took the piglets back home.

Mrs Robinson wanted proper stairs to climb instead of a rope-ladder.

James found the tree was hollow, but there were bees inside!

Mr Robinson put some wet earth on James' face.

Mr Robinson put the bees into a home-made hive.

The rest of the bees were smoked out, and work on the new staircase began.

The new entrance was finished and the staircase was lowered into the tree.

It was much safer than the old rope-ladder.

Early next morning the family was startled by a loud noise.

The SWISS FAMILY ROBINSON

The Robinson family left their home in Switzerland to find a new land. They were ship-wrecked on an island. They lost their donkey. Some loud cries frightened them.

Don't make a sound or you will frighten the wild one.

The donkey had returned with a wild one. It made loud cries. This is what had frightened the family.

I'm coming, Father!

Fritz tempted the donkey with oats. Mr Robinson lassoed the wild one.

Mr Robinson called James to help him tie it to a tree.

Later it got used to being fed by Fritz.

Aren't they pretty? We must get a house built for them.

The rain has started! We must make the store watertight!

Fritz began to train the wild donkey. He decided to call it Lightfoot.

Francis petted the pretty little baby goats.

The rainy season began, and Mr Robinson was worried.

More next week.

The boys made the roof of the storehouse watertight.

Soon everyone was busy packing in the stores.

Then they dashed for shelter as the rain poured down.

The rain was pouring through the tree-house roof. Mr Robinson said they must move to the animals' shed.

The lightning lit the way, but it frightened Mrs Robinson.

While the storm continued they lived in the animals' shed.

Food ran short. The animals had to graze in the storm during the day.

Then the storm died down and the sun came out again.

The family went outside to look around.

The tent was badly damaged by the heavy rain. James ran up with more bad news.

The *Elizabeth* was safe but their other boat was a complete wreck.

James swam out to the *Elizabeth* and baled out some water.

Mr Robinson and James broke up the tub boat for timber.

They put the stores in the cave. It was dry there. The cave would make a shelter for the family, but it was too small.

They decided to make the cave larger.

They dug deeper and deeper into the cave. Then James lost his iron bar.

Mr Robinson hit out one of the rocks and the wall collapsed!

It was another cave! Mr Robinson tested the air.

It was all right to enter the new cave. The family lit torches and explored it.

The new cave would be big enough for them all.

The cave house was finished. Mrs Robinson prepared supper.

Ernest and Fritz went out to catch a turtle for supper.

Fritz turned the turtle on its back. It was caught!

James and Ernest spotted a strange, dark patch in the sea. It was moving quickly towards the beach.

It was a huge shoal of fish. The boys were sent to get baskets.

The shoal of fish had moved closer to the beach. The boys got ready for it.

The fish almost jumped into the baskets!

Mr Robinson and the boys caught a cart-load of fish. They decided to store some.

They cleaned and salted the fish and put it into barrels.

That evening the family had fish for dinner.

Later the boys went out fishing and Ernest spotted an enormous fish.

The boys decided to catch it. Fritz threw a harpoon at it.

After a hard struggle they landed the fish on the rocks.

THE SWISS FAMILY ROBINSON

The Robinson family left their home in Switzerland to find a new land. They were ship-wrecked on an island. Many years passed and no ships came by. Fritz went exploring by canoe.

He wanted to see what was on the other side of the island. He paddled carefully along the coast.

Fritz noticed that the coast was very wild with great jagged cliffs and huge rocks.

Many seabirds flew about him. Then in the clear water Fritz saw some oysters. He collected them.

Some of the oysters contained pearls! Fritz was amazed.

He picked up an albatross which had stunned itself on a rock.

Then he noticed a note which was tied to one of the legs of the bird.

He read the note. It was from an English girl asking for help!

Fritz sent a note back to say that help was coming.

Fritz watched as the bird flew back and wondered what lay out at sea.

Mr Robinson was very relieved to see Fritz safely on his way back to the island in his canoe.

Fritz was eager to show them all the pearls he had found.

But they were of little use to them on a desert island.

Then Fritz showed his father the message for help.

Fritz did not speak about the note again. He showed the family where he found the pearls.

But that night he slipped quietly away and left a note pinned to the tent where he slept.

He had decided to find out who had sent the message for help.

Mr Robinson was not very surprised to see the note.

He told his wife that Fritz would soon be back again.

In the early morning light Fritz paddled his canoe across the calm water. His family were still asleep.

Suddenly, he saw a large volcano in the distance.

He paddled quickly along and came to a rocky coast.

He saw no signs of life as he prepared to land.

Then he discovered a small camping place. Pieces of a wrecked ship lay around.

Fritz explored the undergrowth and came upon a young girl lying fast asleep.

A bird chattered nearby, and she awoke with a start.

Her name was Jenny. Fritz gave her a pineapple.

Then he set off to get the big boat to take Jenny off the rock.

He returned to the island to get a boat to rescue her.
Mrs Robinson had been worried.

Fritz told his parents about the girl.
The family set off for the rock.

Back on the rock Fritz fired
his pistol into the air.

When Jenny came he
introduced her as a boy.

Even Mr Robinson let the younger
boys join in Fritz's joke.

But Fritz gave the game away
when he said "Miss Jenny."

Mrs Robinson made Jenny feel
like one of the family.

Then they all went back to their
home on the island.

Jenny was delighted to be on
their lovely island.

She was rescued just in time. The
rainy season started.

The Robinson family left their home in Switzerland to find a new land but were ship-wrecked on an island. They rescued an English girl named Jenny from a large rock out at sea.

James and Fritz were pleased that the rainy season had ended. They put up a flag on the rock and fired a gun.

To their amazement, they heard an answering shot !

They ran back and told their father, but he hadn't heard it.

James and Fritz fired the gun again and got another reply.

Then they all raced back to the island.

Soon, disguised as natives, Fritz and his father set off.

It did not take long to find the ship. It was anchored in a nearby bay.

As they watched they realised that the ship had stopped to load up with fresh water.

More next week.

Meanwhile, the Captain had spotted Mr Robinson and Fritz. He thought they were natives.

The Robinson family left their home in Switzerland to find a new land, but were ship-wrecked on an island for many years. One day a ship anchored in a nearby bay to pick up water.

I'm sure you frightened them in that get-up!

Fritz and his father had dressed up as natives. But they discovered that the ship was an English one.

So all the family got ready to visit the ship. Mr Robinson, who was a priest, wore his robes.

Jenny, whom they had rescued, went too.

Who can they be? They are white people!

There are ladies, too!

The Captain of the ship was very surprised to see them.

Welcome to the ship Unicorn!

But he welcomed them all to the ship and listened to their adventures.

Welcome to New Switzerland!

Then the family took him to the island.

We have decided not to leave our island.

I will go with Jenny to help find her people.

Fritz decided to go to England to help Jenny find her people.

The family waved goodbye as they left the island.

Some months later.

Some months later a ship stopped near the island.

We are coming back here to live with all of you.

THE END

Jenny and Fritz had married and returned to make their home on the happy island.

FRANK BELLAMY'S ROBIN HOOD

BOOK PALACE BOOKS

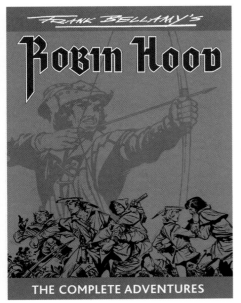

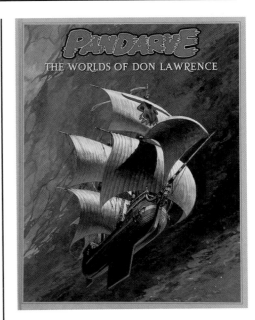

Illustration Art Gallery

Original art from books, magazines, comics and film

Over 3,000 works of art featured online with new art added every month

illustrationartgallery.com
tel: 020 8768 0022
email: art@illustrationartgallery.com